BBC PROMS 95

The BBC presents the Centenary Season of Henry Wood Promenade Concerts

Royal Albert Hall

21 July –
16 September
1995

*Member of the British Arts
Festivals Association*

CONTENTS

*Published by
BBC Concerts Publications
Editorial office:
Room 815, Henry Wood House,
3–6 Langham Place,
London W1A 1AA
Distributed by BBC Books, a division
of BBC Worldwide, 80 Wood Lane,
London W12 0TT*
© BBC 1995. ISBN 0-563-37180-3

Design: John Bury

Advertising: Hugh Muirhead

*Printed by Pindar PLC, Scarborough,
North Yorkshire*

*Front cover and title-page
photographs: Alex von Koettlitz*

BBC
Symphony
Orchestra

At the *heart of the Proms* and the *pulse of music* making throughout the year.

Hear it first.

Join our free mailing list.

Phone: 0171 765 2549

Write to: BBC Symphony Orchestra, FREEPOST LON 3048, London W9 2BR

Photo Illustration by Sam Piyasena

3 BBC RADIO 3 90-93 FM
THE CLASSICAL MUSIC PATRON

FOREWORD

CHARLES HOPKINSON

John Drummond

CELEBRATING THE CENTENARY of the Proms over two seasons may seem like having your cake and eating it, but the inevitable fact of a hundredth season in 1994, and the equally unavoidable fact that the Proms began in 1895, seemed to justify a double celebration. After all, there is a great deal to celebrate; it is not just our own publicists who call the Proms 'the greatest music festival in the world'.

Over the century its leading figures have established not just an annual event, but something that has become part of the life of this country. 1994's retrospective season was a popular success, with the highest attendances of recent years and many fine performances. 1995 must have similar aspirations, but a different focus; if 1994 thrived on history lightly disguised as nostalgia, 1995 must take on the twentieth century and its achievements, and the seeds for the future.

In many of the first hundred seasons there was a Beethoven cycle in the Proms. This year it is Mahler's turn, for he, above all twentieth-century composers, seems to typify our approach to the human spirit: troubled yet triumphant. Though he died before the First World War, it has taken most of the century for his music to gain its present standing. The 1995 Proms include all his symphonies, and most of his other orchestral works with voices. Given that Mahler's symphonies are immense in scale the inevitable result is fewer symphonies by others, particularly from the nineteenth century; but I feel that 'Mahler and Beyond' is a good starting-point for our survey, and provides an appropriate context in which to fit the largest number of new works that the Proms have seen for many years.

However much the availability of music from the past has cast a shadow over living composers, we have nevertheless absorbed many of the great figures of the century: Debussy, Ravel, Stravinsky, Bartók, Prokofiev, Shostakovich, Britten and Lutoslawski are all represented this season, while the centenary of Paul Hindemith and the fiftieth anniversary of the death of Anton Webern give us a chance to reassess their contributions.

But the real concentration is on living composers, ranging from the eighty-six-year-old Elliott Carter, down to fascinating young talents like Julian Anderson and Thomas Adès, by way of established figures like Luciano Berio, Hans Werner Henze and Steve Reich. There are fourteen commissions and fourteen British or London premieres. Discoveries are there to be made and enjoyed – the Chinese composer Tan Dun alongside popular Russian music, the Finnish Kaija Saariaho alongside Szymanowski and Skryabin, James Wood together with traditional Timbila music from Mozambique.

The international nature of composition today is shown by the number of composers who have chosen to live and work far from their places of birth: British composers like Nicholas Maw and Thea Musgrave, long resident in the United States; the New Zealander Lyell Cresswell in Scotland; the Dane Poul Ruders recently living in London; or the Hungarian Peter Eötvös based in the Netherlands. Music has never been so international, nor has it been so alive, so full of excitement or had such success. The past year has seen standing ovations for British composers like Sir Peter Maxwell Davies, Sir Harrison Birtwistle and John Tavener. Instead of being regarded as a 'problem' their music

John Drummond CBE
Director,
BBC Promenade Concerts

Nigel Wilkinson
Senior Proms Producer

Stephen Maddock
Proms Planning Assistant

Nicola Goold
Press Officer

Ann Richards
Marketing Assistant

Liz Russell
Finance Assistant

George Hall
Editor

Karen Cardy
Publications Organiser

Jenny Slater
Publications Officer

UTE KLAPHAKE

Thomas Adès

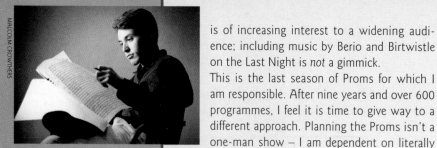

Julian Anderson

Members of the National Youth Orchestra of Great Britain

Wolfgang Sawallisch conducting the Philadelphia Orchestra

is of increasing interest to a widening audience; including music by Berio and Birtwistle on the Last Night is *not* a gimmick.

This is the last season of Proms for which I am responsible. After nine years and over 600 programmes, I feel it is time to give way to a different approach. Planning the Proms isn't a one-man show – I am dependent on literally dozens of colleagues, advisers and friends – but it must reflect something of oneself. Anyone who has the time to look back can see that there are things that I have supported strongly and others that have not found a place at all.

A word about the latter: a lot of great music that I deeply love is difficult to programme in the Albert Hall. Changing attitudes to performing style, or the sheer scale of some works and the amount of time needed to rehearse them, can be reasons for exclusion, as much as taste. But there are things that I consider can find a more appropriate place in the music broadcasting on Radio 3 than in a public forum where you need to sell several thousand tickets every night.

In addition, it is not just the individual work which must justify itself, but its position within programmes that one hopes will intrigue people enough to listen on the radio, watch on television, or pay to come and hear in the hall.

Here, of course, the performers matter as much as the music, both in their selection and realisation. I could never see any point in forcing music on an unwilling interpreter, and perhaps because of this I have had the enthusiastic support of conductors and soloists ready to take on new works, or ones that are infrequently performed.

The total picture, I hope, represents some sort of statement as to what we feel *now* –

not how we felt when we were young, or how we think things were in an age we only know from history books. If music has a future it must be in live performance, that crucible in which, together with the audience, it is carried far beyond the safer atmosphere of the recording studio. No-one who heard Claudio Abbado's performance of Mahler's Ninth Symphony with the Berlin Philharmonic Orchestra last year will ever forget the extraordinary silence that seemed to suspend time itself at its close. It was one of the most moving moments of my life.

In my years at the Proms I have particularly sought to encourage orchestras from outside London, because I believe they benefit from a national and international shop window. This year, seven of Mahler's symphonies are to be performed by regional British orchestras and only one by a foreign group, the Concertgebouw. They return as old friends with Riccardo Chailly, as do the Oslo Philharmonic with Mariss Jansons. There are others from abroad we have not heard for many years, like the Philadelphia Orchestra, with its new music director, Wolfgang Sawallisch, or the Sydney Symphony Orchestra, with its new music director, Edo de Waart.

There are also absolute newcomers. For the first time we have the Academy of Santa Cecilia from Rome with their gifted young conductor Daniele Gatti, in what is also their centenary year. Youth orchestras – a particular favourite of mine – are represented by the National Youth Orchestra of Great Britain under Mark Elder, the renamed European Union Youth Orchestra with Bernard Haitink, and the Junge Deutsche Philharmonie, Germany's national youth orchestra, with Markus Stenz. Graduates from these youth orchestras appear with the Chamber Orchestra of Europe under Nikolaus Harnoncourt, and the Ensemble Modern with Peter Eötvös, in programmes which I find especially intriguing. Old favourites and young favourites are back, and there are a fair number of debuts – some of them on less familiar instruments, from the accordion to the xun. As in my first year there are young British jazz musicians, and there are dancers, in a very un-English *Dido and Æneas*, and in part of a special programme of music from Asia.

In one sense making the Proms is easier than other festivals, simply because people actually *want* to take part. Year after year I destroy family holidays and the well-earned rest that many musicians need with our imperious demands. But artists love the Proms, they love the warmth, the openness and above all the intelligence of the listening audience. After this year I shall no longer be responsible for who is invited, but I am sure that my and the artists' enthusiasm for the Proms will continue as strongly under my successor, Nicholas Kenyon.

Research has shown us that we have a younger audience than other concert series, with a more diverse social mix and more frequent return visits. This stems not just from the programmes, but from the seat prices. I fear that concerts in this country are in danger, not from lack of interest, but from pricing themselves out of reach of their audience. The average concertgoer does not benefit from expense accounts, corporate membership or company hospitality packages. They buy their tickets and come to the Proms as often as they do because they can afford to. The reason for that is that the BBC underwrites the Proms by subsidising the seat prices, which it is only able to do because of the existence of its own orchestras. It would be a very different story were they not to be there. But the Proms are now so successful that the BBC can be said to get them on the cheap, with all expenditure on artists (except the BBC orchestras) covered by income from the box office or by the advertising in our Guide and daily programmes.

These, incidentally, are by far the best value for money of any in the country. I have had the great good fortune throughout my time to have

had George Hall as our Programme Editor, backed up by Karen Cardy and Jenny Slater – a small but marvellous team who seem capable of incorporating even the latest last-minute change, whilst making the

STEVE J. SHERMAN

Venancio Mbande and The Hague Percussion Group

Proms Guide a pleasure to use and to keep. In a world where broadcasting organisations are often accused of overmanning, the Proms team remains the smallest I know anywhere for an enterprise of this kind. The commitment of my staff in planning (Stephen Maddock), finance (Liz Russell) and publicity (Nicola Goold and Ann Richards) has been remarkable. The success of the Proms in recent years is as much theirs as anyone's.

A final word for my other colleagues. Nigel Wilkinson has co-ordinated the broadcasting side of the Proms for the last five seasons. His unflappability is a necessary counterbalance to my own more volatile approach! The BBC's regional orchestras have been a joy to work with, steadily raising their standards and achievements. The BBC Symphony Orchestra is the workhorse of the Proms, and of the many decisions that I have taken over the past nine years, the appointment of Andrew Davis as its Chief Conductor seems to me the happiest.

It would be uncharacteristic of me to go without a final grumble, so here it is. This year, on the Last Night, could we listen to the music without extraneous noises? By all means sing when required, sway about, dress up if you must, but leave those balloons, claxons and pop-guns at home. The music and the speech need to be heard.

I look forward to you joining us for the Centenary Season.

John Drummond CBE
Director, BBC Promenade Concerts

LINDA CORBETT

Opera Atelier's production of 'Dido and Æneas'

DROOPY & BROWNS BY ANGELA HOLMES

Photograph: Anthony Crickmay

DAYWEAR

CONCERT DRESSES

WEDDING GOWNS

MILLINERY

99 ST MARTINS LANE
LONDON WC2
0171 379 4514

1-2 PULTENEY BRIDGE
BATH
01225 463796

37-39 FREDERICK STREET
EDINBURGH
0131 225 1019

21 STONEGATE
YORK
01904 621458

16-18 QUEEN VICTORIA STREET
LEEDS
0113 234 1143

FOR YOUR ON STAGE
&
OFF STAGE WARDROBE

Having been in the UK for over a hundred years, we're very much part of the community. We spend millions every year on environment, education and care programmes, especially for young people. We encourage equal opportunities and employment training. And we support the National Gallery. All this is part of our policy of investing in future generations. **Putting the next generation first.**

ALBERT RENEWED

Robert Hewison previews developments at the Proms' Official Residence

EW PEOPLE can have failed to notice the changes that have taken place in the appearance of the Royal Albert Hall in recent years. If the brass seems shinier, the lights brighter, and the staff more confident and welcoming in their red plush uniforms, that is because they are. In fact, more than £5 million has been spent on general improvements since 1990 – though only a fraction of this technical work is visible to the visitor.

But these changes are as nothing to those that are now being planned. In essence the building is going to be turned round, and the basement turned upside down – all without closing down for more than a few weeks in a year. During this period of intensive renovation the Hall will see more activity, not less, more performances, not fewer.

The first major visible improvement comes next year, when the seats in the Balcony will be taken out to be replaced with ones that will bring them up to 'dress circle' standards. This £1 million scheme is being funded by an appeal to the seatholders of the 'Corporation of the Hall of Arts

An early design for the Hall of Arts and Sciences, 1869

and Sciences' which was formed in 1866 as a charity to build and manage the Hall, and whose members have had certain rights to occupy 1,300 of the 5,200 seats in the auditorium since the building opened in 1871. Since none of these seats is in the Balcony, a special visit was arranged so that members of the Corporation could see the problem for themselves, and they were quick to appreciate the benefit to the Hall as a whole that the refurbishment will bring.

Although replacing 1,800 seats is equivalent to renewing the seating of an entire modern concert hall, this is a relatively minor project compared to the work that will begin in the bowels of the building in 1997. At present the Hall has two major backstage defects. Everything needed for performances has to be unloaded outside in the road and then manhandled into the Hall through public areas. At the same time the arrangements in the basement are such that the dressing-rooms are not on the level of the stage but on the floor below that, and facilities leave a lot to be desired for the sometimes hundreds of performers who have to use them. (It is not for nothing that the Director of the Proms, John Drummond, has called this area 'the black hole of Kensington'.)

In 1997 all this will begin to change. In 1993, thanks to making a healthy surplus the year before (as a charity the Corporation cannot distribute any profits, only reinvest them – which is how it has survived without public subsidy), the area covered by the south steps, and all the substantial garage space below it, was reacquired for £0.5 million. A tunnel will be driven underneath the south steps to below the auditorium large enough for all the trucks and pantechnicons needed to transport the equipment demanded by modern performances to be moved in and out, so that they can deliver their loads without disturbing the public – thus creating a much faster turnaround between performances. At the same time, if current architectural studies prove fruitful, the dressing-rooms will be brought up to stage level, and new kitchens and technical areas for improved ventilation will be installed. Promenaders will find they have much easier and more direct access to the Arena, with better bars and facilities all round.

Having turned the basement area on its head – though, it is hoped, without interrupting performances – the plan then is to turn the Hall round by shifting the main

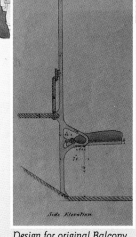

Design for original Balcony seating

Below: *The Royal Horticultural Gardens, with the Albert Hall and Albert Memorial in the background (1871)*

Below left: *Colonel Scott's plan for the Hall and surrounding area, c1866*

Original drawing of exterior frieze

The proposed new South Entrance

Far right: *The State Concert at the Hall, 1873*

entrance from the north, Kensington Gore side, to the south. This is a return to the original configuration of the building, for the present, somewhat forlorn south porch was once just a connection between the Hall and the huge iron and glass conservatory of the Royal Horticultural Society, whose gardens lay to the south. This served as a vast foyer, and was connected in turn to the pedestrian tunnels that lead to South Kensington station. The proposal for 1998 is to rebuild the south porch to match the northern one, and make this the new entrance area, with ticketing and merchandising, and a 150- to 250-seater restaurant and brasserie on the Grand Tier level. The east and west porches will also be glazed in and converted into bars.

The interior of the Hall will have seen further changes by 1998. There are plans to improve the Gallery, to install more public lifts, and to create a more efficient and flexible lighting system. The major proposal – which is still only tentative – may prove more controversial. Since the acoustic 'mushrooms' were installed in the 1960s they have become very much part of the building, but the science of

acoustics has moved on since then, and there are proposals to study the installation to deal with the celebrated echo. These could not only be in a shape more harmonious with that of the Hall, they might also be transparent, so that the ceiling would be once more revealed.

It goes without saying that the immediate surroundings of the Hall will also have to change. Once there is access from underground, the car parks surrounding the Hall will be closed, and the whole area pedestrianised, from the south steps to Kensington Gore. There have been proposals to take this further by lowering the road and creating a terrace that would lead directly to the foot of the Albert Memorial – thus directly linking the two monuments to the memory of Prince Albert, inspirer of the Great Exhibition of 1851 and of the 'music hall' that now bears his name. One can see the logic but also the difficulties of this scheme, and at present it is not part of the development plan.

Where the Royal Albert Hall will be reaching out, however, is in its links with the other cultural

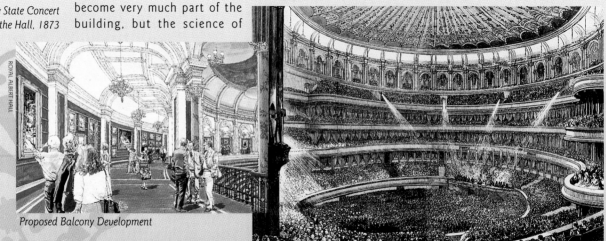

Proposed Balcony Development

It's not just a concert, it's the
Royal Philharmonic Orchestra
at the **Royal Albert Hall**

Concerts include

Verdi ***Requiem***

Walton ***Belshazzar's Feast***

Elgar ***Dream of Gerontius***

Berlioz ***Damnation of Faust***

For a free brochure giving full details of the concerts and dates, please send the form below to:
Marketing Department, Royal Philharmonic Orchestra, FREEPOST (no stamp necessary), London EC1B 1RP

Please send me information about the Royal Philharmonic Orchestra's concerts at the Royal Albert Hall:

NAME:

ADDRESS:

POSTCODE:

DAYTIME TEL:

DATE:

Royal Philharmonic
Britain's and Classic FM's
national orchestra

Funded by
THE
ARTS
COUNCIL
OF ENGLAND

Sir Edward Downes

Valery Gergiev

Sir Charles Mackerras

Andrew Litton

Yuri Temirkanov

Your first opportunity to enjoy a winter series at the Royal Albert Hall – with concerts conducted by

a world of music

Founded on the great European traditions of instrument making and music publishing, the Boosey & Hawkes Group is today one of the world's foremost music companies.

Our international roster of twentieth-century composers is unrivalled and our instruments are played by performers throughout the world. In both advanced and developing countries we are exercising an important influence, as more people turn to music as a popular leisure pursuit.

In the field of music education, we are firmly committed to helping develop future generations of musicians by providing them with access to instruments and printed music of the highest quality.

From school concerts to the Proms, from bandrooms to opera houses, on radio and television, Boosey & Hawkes helps the world to enjoy the priceless gift of music.

BOOSEY&HAWKES

institutions that surround it: the Royal College of Art, the Royal Geographical Society, the Royal College of Music and the rest of what has become known as 'Albertopolis'. Patrick Deuchar, the Hall's chief executive since 1989, says that 'you have got a most wonderful collection of cultural institutions around here that are just waiting to blend together. We have got to be, as it were, the hub of the wheel. Some people might say that all the Hall needs is a lick of paint and lower prices, but that would be just to carry on as before. We have to make this beautiful Hall more beautiful, and this busy Hall more busy'. It is also Deuchar's aspiration in the long term to be able to do more about the commitment of 'the Hall of Arts and Sciences' to science as well as the arts.

By installing better backstage facilities Deuchar hopes to be able to put on more than 300 shows a year, and with more to offer front of house to run a daytime open foyer programme, as on the South Bank. This year there will be 280 performances, and the Hall has moved into a new phase by offering a London home to the Royal Philharmonic Orchestra. On 25 September the RPO will present the first of ten concerts in a debut season, with a full opening season to come in 1996–7.

The question that must be asked, however, is how all this is to be paid for. Piece by piece and year by year, these improvements will cost somewhere between £30 and £40 million, if not more, and the Hall has no public subsidy of any kind. But 1995 is the year that the funds from the National Lottery come on stream, and as an arts facility and a Grade One listed building the Hall qualifies for money from both the Arts Council and the National Heritage Memorial Fund. Patrick Deuchar was still preparing his bid when I spoke to him, and he did not take lottery money for granted. The improvements so far have been funded from the surpluses the Hall itself has generated, and that programme will continue. But as Deuchar put it: 'If we want everything done in six years, then it is down to the Lottery. If we want it done in twenty-six years, the hall will do it itself'.

The rather grand-sounding Royal Albert Hall also likes to think of itself as 'the Nation's Village Hall', a place where there is a commitment to excellence without élitism (which is a good way of describing the Proms). With the luck of the lottery behind it, the Hall will become a nineteenth-century national monument fit for the twenty-first century.

Original drawing of exterior frieze

Background:
Cutaway plan of the Hall
BUSINESS DESIGN PARTNERSHIP

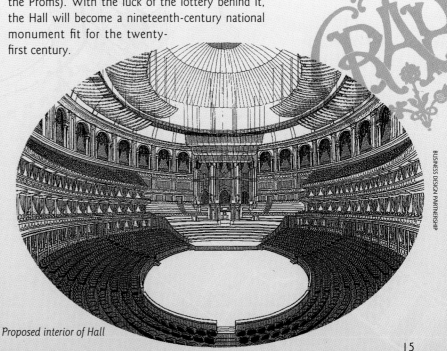

Proposed interior of Hall

BUSINESS DESIGN PARTNERSHIP

ORPHEUS IGNORED?

This year sees the 300th anniversary of the death of Henry Purcell, long acknowledged as one of the greatest composers this country has produced.

Lindsay Kemp wonders whether we really appreciate him today

WHEN I WAS SMALL and first interested in music, I fell in love with the *Young Person's Guide to the Orchestra*. 'Who's your favourite composer?', adults would ask, to which I would reply, 'Benjamin Britten'. The reaction was often approving nods from those impressed that one so young should show appreciation for such a sophisticated composer (and a modern one at that).

What I should have answered, I later realised, was 'Henry Purcell'. It was, after all, his robust tune – composed for a gruesome play called *Abdelazer* and orchestrated so nobly by Britten – that had really grabbed my attention.

But would that answer have drawn the same response? Would Purcell – composer of the famous *Trumpet Voluntary* (actually by Jeremiah Clarke), of *Nymphs and Shepherds*, and of various little minuets and preludes I had learnt on the piano – have seemed such a precocious choice for a little boy?

I hardly think so. For the truth is that while Purcell is a figure whom musicians may respect for his compositional skill, even revere for his unique brand of expressiveness, his highly individual sense of melancholy and his unmatched gift for word-setting, people are still disinclined to think of him as a really great artist.

It is a misconception that afflicts Baroque music in general, but it seems to affect this composer especially. Vaughan Williams was of the opinion that even as we recognise Purcell as one of this country's finest composers, we only pay him lip-service, because our actual knowledge of his music is so slight (even today some of his works are only just being recorded for the first time). Another way of looking at it is that our admiration is rooted in received opinion, in a kind of condescension, rather than in true comprehension. We know we ought to acknowledge him, but we do not know *why*.

Is this because the Restoration England in which Purcell grew up appears to us in many ways so superficial? When we think of the atmosphere sur-

Purcell's London, viewed from Southwark
MUSEUM OF LONDON

Henry Purcell

rounding the court of Charles II, or of Restoration comedy, we see a world which seems to value cleverness above profundity, wit over substance. When we note the triviality of some of the texts Purcell set to music (such as the odes he composed for royal birthdays and homecomings), we see a further reflection of this.

Yet the return of the monarchy in 1660 also heralded the age of Newton and Wren – a time of excess maybe, but one which, after the austerities of Cromwell's Commonwealth, provided the sheer opulence and optimism needed to release the talents of such men ('like ships waiting at high tide', as Lord Clark once put it).

In Purcell, born one year before the Restoration and brought up right at the centre of court musical life (his father was a musician in the royal service) in which Henry was to spend his entire life, we see much of the spirit of the age. As a supplier of church music for the Chapel Royal at the start of his composing career, he was able to write with all the splendour and pomp a patron as self-regarding as

King Charles could wish for.

Yet right from the beginning there is also great musical sophistication and depth: in many early church compositions – such as the deeply expressive settings of the funeral sentences or the anthems *Remember not, Lord, our offences* and *Hear my prayer, O Lord* – we find Purcell showing off the strength of his talent and individualism; and even after Charles's death in 1685, the royal taste for jaunty church music accompanied by instruments is reflected to unparalleled effect in the magnificence of *My heart is inditing*, the anthem Purcell wrote for the coronation of his successor, James II.

One is reminded of the words of the composer Thomas Tudway, one of the few people to have left us with so much as a hint of personal reminiscence, who recalled that Purcell 'had a most commendable ambition of exceeding every one of his time, and he succeeded in it without contradiction'.

Right: *Sir Isaac Newton (1642–1727) by Sir Godfrey Kneller (1646–1723)*
NATIONAL PORTRAIT GALLERY, LONDON

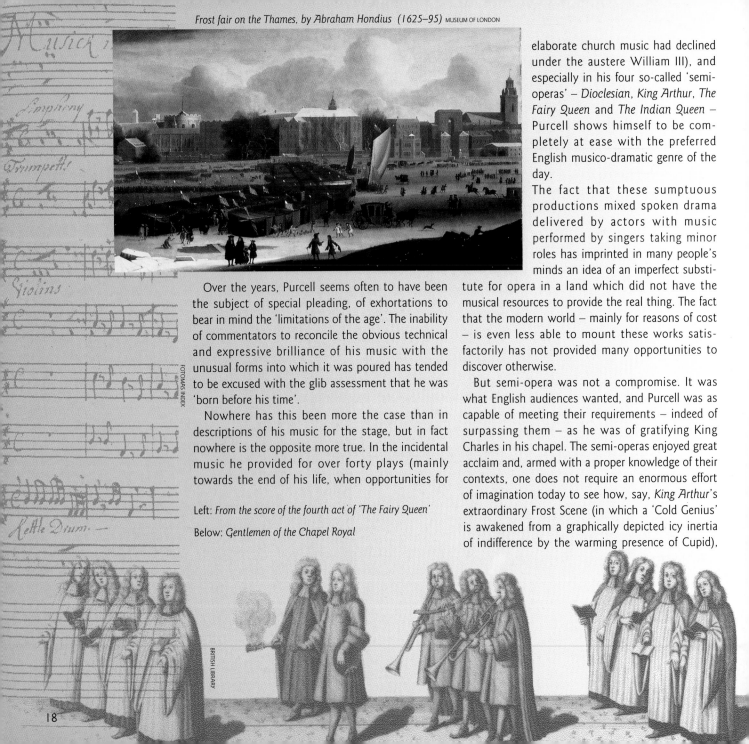

Frost fair on the Thames, by Abraham Hondius (1625–95) MUSEUM OF LONDON

elaborate church music had declined under the austere William III), and especially in his four so-called 'semi-operas' – *Dioclesian*, *King Arthur*, *The Fairy Queen* and *The Indian Queen* – Purcell shows himself to be completely at ease with the preferred English musico-dramatic genre of the day.

The fact that these sumptuous productions mixed spoken drama delivered by actors with music performed by singers taking minor roles has imprinted in many people's minds an idea of an imperfect substitute for opera in a land which did not have the musical resources to provide the real thing. The fact that the modern world – mainly for reasons of cost – is even less able to mount these works satisfactorily has not provided many opportunities to discover otherwise.

But semi-opera was not a compromise. It was what English audiences wanted, and Purcell was as capable of meeting their requirements – indeed of surpassing them – as he was of gratifying King Charles in his chapel. The semi-operas enjoyed great acclaim and, armed with a proper knowledge of their contexts, one does not require an enormous effort of imagination today to see how, say, *King Arthur*'s extraordinary Frost Scene (in which a 'Cold Genius' is awakened from a graphically depicted icy inertia of indifference by the warming presence of Cupid),

Over the years, Purcell seems often to have been the subject of special pleading, of exhortations to bear in mind the 'limitations of the age'. The inability of commentators to reconcile the obvious technical and expressive brilliance of his music with the unusual forms into which it was poured has tended to be excused with the glib assessment that he was 'born before his time'.

Nowhere has this been more the case than in descriptions of his music for the stage, but in fact nowhere is the opposite more true. In the incidental music he provided for over forty plays (mainly towards the end of his life, when opportunities for

Left: *From the score of the fourth act of 'The Fairy Queen'*

Below: *Gentlemen of the Chapel Royal*

FOTOMAS INDEX

BRITISH LIBRARY

or its great final-act patriotic masque showing England in former and future greatness, would have excited contemporary audiences.

Even Purcell's acknowledged masterpiece, his only through-composed opera *Dido and Æneas*, has suffered from qualification. The word 'flawed' has often been used. Certainly a dramatically untidy libretto is not a help, while the opera's brevity, and the fact that it was long thought to have been composed for performance in 1689 by the inmates of a girls' boarding school, has inclined people to take the view that, once again, Purcell was battling against restrictions in budget and performer ability.

Recent scholarship, however, has suggested that it was first conceived and performed several years earlier, as a court masque, and that as such it is a different animal, with different aspirations, from a miniature, almost 'imitation' opera. What is certain is that it contains dramatic music of peerless quality and truth, in the space of an hour taking in Dido's anguished longings for and happy acceptance of Æneas as a lover, the jealous connivings of her enemies, and finally her unforgettable lament – without doubt one of the most moving passages of music ever composed.

Purcell's death at the age of only thirty-six was greatly lamented by his contemporaries. Among the most eloquent epitaphs were musical odes composed by distinguished colleagues such as John Blow and Jeremiah Clarke. Others stuck to words whose sincerity is reinforced by their simplicity. 'A greater musical genius England never had', declared one writer; 'Gone is the Glory of our Age' bewailed another.

In this tercentenary year, which is also Radio 3's British Music Year, such remarks will be repeated many times, their sentiments echoed just as often. But if the celebrations are to achieve anything, it must be a regard born of understanding. Perhaps then Purcell will be seen for what he was: a rounded artistic personality equally able to excel in church, in the playhouse, at court and in the chamber, and whose music spoke both of his age and of the timeless subjects of all art.

The Lincoln's Inn Fields Theatre, where 'Dido and Æneas' received its first public performance in 1700

VICTORIA & ALBERT MUSEUM

Below: *'The Vision of Æneas in the Elysian Fields', by Sebastiano Conca (1680–1764)*

PRIVATE COLLECTION / BRIDGEMAN ART LIBRARY

19

HOW TO SAY **JAGUAR** IN ITALIAN:

"THE MOST BEAUTIFUL SALOON CAR IN THE WORLD."

MILAN INTERNATIONAL COMPETITION

226

The new Jaguar XJ Series

JAGUAR

DON'T DREAM IT. DRIVE IT.

For more information on the new XJ Series call **0800 708060**

Fairest Isle

BBC RADIO 3

'FAIREST ISLE', RADIO 3'S YEAR-LONG
EXPLORATION OF BRITISH MUSIC
AND CULTURE, IS ACCOMPANIED BY
A MAJOR NEW BOOK CELEBRATING
900 YEARS OF BRITAIN'S RICH
AND DIVERSE MUSICAL HERITAGE.

*Leading writers on British music have contributed
to this lavishly illustrated 136-page volume
which also lists recommended books and recordings.*

*Explore British Composers including
Dunstable, Tallis, Byrd, Purcell, Elgar,
Delius, Vaughan Williams, Britten
and many less familiar names, from the
12th-century hermit St Godric,
to contemporary figures such
as James MacMillan.*

The book costs £6.99 and is available from
all good bookshops. To order post-free,
please telephone 01483 268888.

CENTRAL EUROPEAN

Paul Banks considers Mahler's journey to the centre of our listening experience

THIRTY YEARS AGO, when computers filled rooms and could be communicated with only through punched cards, the notion that a small desk-top machine in the home might be able to display the information from a substantial dictionary of musical instruments, together with colour images (some of them moving) and hi-fi sound illustrations, would have seemed pretty incredible. About as likely as the possibility that in such a dictionary a symphony by Gustav Mahler would be used to exemplify the sound of the nineteenth-century orchestra.

By the early 1960s Mahler's music was certainly becoming more familiar, but he remained a marginal figure for most concert-goers. Indeed it was only in that decade that many of his greatest works were heard for the first time at the Proms. Today the CD-ROM has arrived with illustrations from Mahler's *oeuvre*, and the 1995 Proms offer audiences the chance to experience virtually every note of his output during one season.

Such a prospect would undoubtedly have amazed the critic Eric Blom, who in the early 1950s declared on behalf of the British public that 'we just don't want Mahler here'. It would have flabbergasted his anonymous predecessor who, having heard the first performance in the country of a Mahler symphony, declared: 'the music struck me as utterly impossible ... sixty minutes of dreadful monotony and weakness'. The conductor responsible for provoking this eruption of venom was Sir Henry J. Wood,

Far left: *'The Knight', detail from the Beethoven Frieze by Gustav Klimt (1862–1918), said to be a portrait of Mahler*

Left: *The British premiere of Mahler's Eighth Symphony at the Queen's Hall, 1930. Henry Wood conducts the BBC Symphony Orchestra*

ÖSTERREICHISCHE GALERIE, VIENNA/BRIDGEMAN ART LIBRARY

BBC

who included Mahler's First Symphony in the 1903 Prom season. Fortunately Sir Henry was not one to be put off by critical dyspepsia, and in the years up to the First World War he conducted the Fourth and Seventh symphonies, *The Song of the Earth* and the Adagietto of the Fifth in his concerts.

Although he had neither the inclination (nor, one suspects, the opportunity) to mount a sustained campaign on Mahler's behalf, as was done with success by Willem Mengelberg in Amsterdam, Wood continued his advocacy of Mahler's music after the war, most notably in mounting the first British performance of the immense Eighth Symphony in 1930. The performance may not have been beyond reproach, but whatever its shortcomings it made a 'tremendous impression' on at least one member of the audience who was to reflect the impact of Mahler's music in a number of his own compositions – Benjamin Britten.

It is very unlikely that this prodigious work would have been heard at all without the financial and administrative support of the BBC, then a very young but already formidable organisation, and by the time of the performance its Director of Music was another conductor sympathetic to Mahler, Adrian Boult. In the years that followed the BBC played an increasingly important role in nurturing interest in the composer, particularly through its broadcasts of works not yet heard with any frequency in British concert halls. That process culminated in the Mahler Centenary celebrations in 1960, but the Corporation's most enduring (though still controversial) contribution to our experience of Mahler stemmed not from the fine performances it could mount, but from the rich resources of critical astuteness, adventurousness and scholarly acumen embodied in its music staff. In December 1960, with Robert Simpson's encouragement, Deryck Cooke

Deryck Cooke

broadcast a lecture about Mahler's unfinished Tenth Symphony in which an explanation of the work's history preceded the premiere of a performing version of most of the work by the Philharmonia Orchestra conducted by Berthold Goldschmidt, thereby allowing a wide audience the opportunity to hear the ineffably beautiful music of the symphony's finale for the first time. Clearly this was no mere musicological exercise, but a profoundly moving experience. There had been other completions of the symphony, and others have been made since, but it was Cooke's version, finished in 1964, which for many listeners established the work as the apt conclusion of the composer's symphonic output.

In the 1960s perceptions of Mahler's significance shifted dramatically – no longer did he occupy a peripheral place in the concert hall, but was moving steadily rather closer to the centre. Just as striking was the change in attitude of recording companies. Before the late 1940s Mahler's music posed almost insuperable technical problems – his huge symphonies occupied large numbers of 78rpm shellac discs, and his brilliant and varied orchestration (sometimes using off-stage instruments) made great demands on the skills of recording engineers. Nevertheless attempts were made to capture the music on disc, beginning with the acoustic recording of the Second Symphony conducted by Oskar Fried in 1923. The culmination of this first phase were probably the live recordings of *The Song of the Earth* and the Ninth Symphony made by Bruno Walter and the Vienna Philharmonic Orchestra in the

Berthold Goldschmidt, who conducted the premiere of Cooke's performing version of Mahler's Tenth Symphony at the Proms in 1964

Caricature of Mahler at the time of the Sixth

1930s. Mahler's songs were less problematic, and the recording of *Kindertotenlieder* made by Heinrich Rehkemper and Jascha Horenstein in 1928 remains one of the very greatest.

The advent of the LP and magnetic tape transformed the ability of recording companies to market Mahler's music. Yet the process was slow. With notable exceptions (such as Bruno Walter's Decca recording of *The Song of the Earth* with Kathleen Ferrier and Julius Patzak), it was less famous conductors and orchestras who tackled the symphonies on disc for the first time. The adoption of stereo recording (which finally offered the ability to reproduce the complex landscape of Mahler's sound-world) was followed by the numerous performances of Mahler in 1960. Soon there were two complete cycles of the symphonies being recorded (by Leonard Bernstein and Rafael Kubelík) and listeners no longer had to rely on the whim of concert promoters to gain access to Mahler's music.

Greater availability certainly played a role in the explosion of interest in Mahler: the views of critics and commentators could be weighed against the music itself – and in many cases were found to be wanting. Mahler's music challenges listeners and their preconceptions of what a symphony ought to be. From the miraculous opening of the First Symphony onwards, Mahler showed a willingness to reassess how such a work should sound,

Portrait by Emil Orlik (1870–1932)

what sort of themes it might use, and on what sort of scale it should be constructed. The early symphonies often adopt a wonderfully transparent, clean-edged approach to orchestral texture, use themes that appear grotesque, ironic, banal or sentimental, and do so over an extended time-span. On a first hearing all of this can be very disconcerting – as the critic of the First Symphony evidently found in 1903! – but better acquaintance reinforced appreciation of the phenomenal imagination with which Mahler exploits the symphony orchestra, the profound seriousness of his works which underpins his use of apparently 'unsymphonic' themes, and established that, given their content, his symphonies *have* to be big. The result was that Mahler's music no longer seemed monotonous and weak but exciting and powerful.

Alongside a deeper awareness of how Mahler composed came a greater sympathy for *why* he composed. He had no doubt that music could communicate to listeners, and deployed all his technical resources to express clearly a personal and intense

Caricature of the premiere of Mahler's First Symphony in 1888. Mahler blows into the horn

Gustav Mahler

 Judith Weir

 Poul Ruders

 Sir Peter
Maxwell Davies

 Kaija Saariaho

 Jean Sibelius

 Leonard Bernstein

 Igor Stravinsky

 Witold
Lutoslawski

 Benedict Mason

 Manuel de Falla

 George Antheil

 Sir Edward Elgar

 Tan Dun

 John Tavener

 Elliott Carter

 Carl Nielsen

 Thea Musgrave

Chester Music, Novello and our sister companies
are honoured to publish works by these composers,
who all feature in this very special Proms season.

Chester Music
Established 1860
Novello & Company
Established 1830
G Schirmer/AMP
Established 1861
Edition Wilhelm Hansen
Established 1857
Edwin Ashdown
Established 1882
Unión Musical Ediciones
Established 1900
8/9 Frith Street London W1V 5TZ
Telephone: 0171-434 0066 Fax: 0171-287 6329
The Music Sales Group.
Bringing you the world's best music.

CHESTER MUSIC

TOWER
RECORDS · VIDEO · BOOKS

In the rain forests of Brazil, a single drop of water can contain dozens of life forms... A square metre of ground can have hundreds of plant types... An acre of land is home to many thousands of animal and plant species...

This is bio-diversity – an almost infinite pool of life, revolving, stimulating, always moving. It is just this diversity which ensures the success of the forest, and diversity is the key at Tower.

Here you'll find a richer and more varied range of classical recordings than any other record store can offer. A lush forest of human expression, deep and exciting, created by artists from throughout the world and up through the centuries. Our friendly, knowledgeable staff are always at hand to act as guides.

A single note can be played in so many ways, and heard in so many more, that a lifetime of listening can never be enough to sample Tower's classical selection.

So much to hear, so little time, so why not start now?

If you can't make it into the store, please call our
Mail Order service on (0171) 287 1510 or Fax (0171) 434 2766

THE TOWER DIFFERENCE IS SELECTION

Mahler by Anton Wagner

A doodle on blotting paper by Mahler

of art must always be the ultimate liberation from and transcendence of sorrow'. Most of his works offer some sort of narrative which can be understood as such an overcoming. In many, the culmination is a direct expression of spiritual joy; the only exception is the profoundly tragic Sixth Symphony. Even in the last three symphonic works, *The Song of the Earth* and the Ninth and Tenth symphonies, all written under the shadow of death, the concluding pages balance feelings of regret and loss with an unforgettable awareness of the beauty of the world. Faced with the ultimate negation Mahler composed with unfailing imagination and artistic integrity, offering us a vision of transcendence.

Mahler said in 1893 that 'It isn't enough to judge a work of art by its content; we must consider its total image, in which content and form are indissolubly blended. It is this which determines its value, its power of survival, and its immortality'. Today few would deny that Mahler's own music has proved its powers of survival.

experience of the human condition. That experience included a particularly searing exploration of the dark side of the soul, profound uncertainties and anxieties, and it may well be this that struck a chord in a world which, in the 1960s, sometimes seemed on the brink of destruction. The sources of our uncertainty may now be less clearly defined, but it seems that it is this aspect of Mahler's world that continues to grip our attention most powerfully.

Yet to do justice to the composer we should perhaps remember that he once declared that 'the aim

FASCINATING EMILIA

Mark Audus introduces this season's Glyndebourne opera and its 300-year-old heroine

Leoš Janáček (1854–1928)

JANÁČEK MUSEUM, BRNO

SINCE THE FIRST FLUSH of her youth, Emilia Marty has known and outlasted three different centuries and a clutch of lovers whose number is unspecified only because unknown. Nor, with one exception, has she been at all fond of any of them. In fact, she is 337 years old. She first saw the light of day in the late sixteenth century in the Prague of Rudolf II, but we meet her in a lawyer's chambers in the Prague of 1922.

Emilia Marty is the heroine of Janáček's extraordinary penultimate opera, *The Makropulos Case*. She was born Elina Makropulos, daughter of the Emperor's personal physician, and it is from this that her longevity derives: Makropulos was commanded to elaborate an elixir of life which he then tested on the young Elina. She has changed her name many times over the years, but always retained the same initials, E.M.

Janáček had a penchant for unlikely subjects for his operas, taken from both likely and unlikely places: a series of newspaper cartoons on animal life inspired *The Cunning Little Vixen*, whilst his final opera, *From the House of the Dead*, was based on Dostoyevsky's pseudo-autobiographical novel about life in a Siberian prison camp.

The origins of *The Makropulos Case* were, like those of his first operatic success, *Jenůfa*, theatrical, but there the similarities end. Unlike the earlier tale of Moravian folk life, Karel Čapek's play is set in the sophisticated surroundings of contemporary Prague, with all the trappings of modernity: lawyer's files, telephones, theatre props, fur coats and hotel rooms. Čapek intended his conversational comedy as a refutation of the Utopian ideal of scientific progress, its cold, disillusioned heroine disproving the equation of unlimited life with increased wisdom and happiness.

Unpromising as this material might seem for operatic treatment – Čapek himself had doubts about its suitability, particularly the intricate legal wranglings which take up so much of the action – Janáček succeeds marvellously in turning an ironic conversation piece into a moving account of the heroine's reconciliation to the realities of life and death.

His approach shifts between the humour and incongruousness of busy modern-day characters, to the ageless – though intensely personal – conflicts of Emilia's inner life. It is this blend which brings out the pathos of her situation: disabused and cynical as a result of her all-too-long experience of human affairs, she is coolly indifferent to her fellow men, but increasingly and painfully aware of the real nature of her plight.

KUNSTHISTORISCHES MUSEUM, VIENNA / BRIDGEMAN ART LIBRARY

Rudolf II (1552–1612)

'Poor 300-year-old beauty!', wrote Janáček in December 1925, shortly after finishing the opera. 'People thought she was a thief, a liar, an unfeeling animal. "Beast", "canaille" they called her. They wanted to strangle her. And her fault? That she had to live long. I was sorry for her.' And it was Janáček who devised the final resolution in which Marty, having recovered the secret formula for the elixir of life, realises she no longer wants it and, in the composer's words, 'crumples up'. She has earned forgiveness from the other characters, as well as release from and reconciliation with life. She has also, in an almost Wagnerian manner, obtained redemption.

The Czech actress Zdena Herfortová as Emilia Marty in Čapek's play
JOSEF KRATOCHVIL

Below left: Karel Čapek

By thus transforming Čapek's play to include an individual and tragic element, the idea of the discovery of a personal quest and the emotions this releases, Janáček achieved the summation of all his earlier operatic heroines – Jenůfa, Katya Kabanova and the Vixen. Significantly, his final opera, *From the House of the Dead*, is written, with one small exception, for an all-male cast. In Marty, he had encapsulated all that fascinated him most in his female characters.

Despite Marty's commanding presence – she is on stage for most of the opera's ninety minutes – Janáček draws the other players in the story with all the skill of a composer at the height of his powers. He drastically pruned their more speculative speeches, but succeeded through sharp characterisation and the skilful interplay of dialogue in illuminating their many traits, from the grunting legalisms of the lawyer Kolenatý and the senile ranting of Marty's one-time lover Hauk, to the frustrated passion of Marty's great-great-grandson Gregor and the fragile innocence of the young Kristina.

The result is perhaps his most perfect opera. *The Makropulos Case* may lack the searing lyricism of its predecessors, but the command of characterisation, depth of emotional insight and sophisticated orchestral writing make it one of the outstanding operas of this century.

Given its strange and uncompromising subject-matter, it is perhaps not surprising that *Makropulos* has never been among the most popular of Janáček's works. At its premiere in Brno on 18 December 1926, however, it scored a triumph, despite worries over the technical difficulty of the music.

A few days later Janáček wrote to his friend Kamila Stösslová: 'That "icy one" [ie Emilia Marty] had unsuspected

'Top Hats' from 'The Twenties Remembered Again', by Erté (1892–1990)

PRAGUE NATIONAL MUSEUM, THEATRE DIVISION

constant renewal of life. With his transformation of Čapek's dry and pointed satire he goes a step further: to show that the joy of life lies in its span, even its brevity, in its sense of a journey begun, pursued and ended.

Life has colour and shape, but direction too. And if life's curve is flattened out, it is not only deprived of shape, but drained of all colour, the colour of sensation and of emotion. Perhaps, too, if life becomes an unbending linear progression it also loses its direction. This is Janáček's vision.

To extend human life to 300 years or more would be to rob it of the very vitality and pettiness that make it what it is, replacing them with limitless extension and limitless emptiness that would know neither good nor bad, simply indifference.

And perhaps it was Janáček's recognition of his own idiosyncrasies, as both man and composer, that led him to write some of his grandest music for the death of his ultimate heroine.

Stage designs for the premiere of The Makropulos Case', 1928

Right: Janáček taking a curtain call

success! To the extent that everybody had cold shivers down their spines. They say it is my greatest work'. It was the last of his operas that the composer heard premiered.

Fifteen months later, on 1 March 1928, Janáček attended the first staging in Prague, where, despite his uneasy relationship with the Czech capital, it was also well received. With the exception of one German production in 1929, it was not until the Janáček renaissance of the post-war years that the score gained a wider hearing. It was first heard in England in a Sadler's Wells production of 1964; thirty-one years on, the new Glyndebourne production is the first in this country in the original Czech.

Emilia Marty's story is one of the strangest but also most moving and uplifting in all opera. Here, close to the end of his own life, Janáček confronts his audience with one of the most searching mysteries of all, the nature of human mortality. In *The Cunning Little Vixen* he affirmed his faith in the

JANÁČEK MUSEUM, BRNO

Glyndebourne Festival Opera perform The Makropulos Case *under Andrew Davis in Prom 48*

CLIVE BARDA

Josephine Barstow as Emilia Marty, ENO, 1982

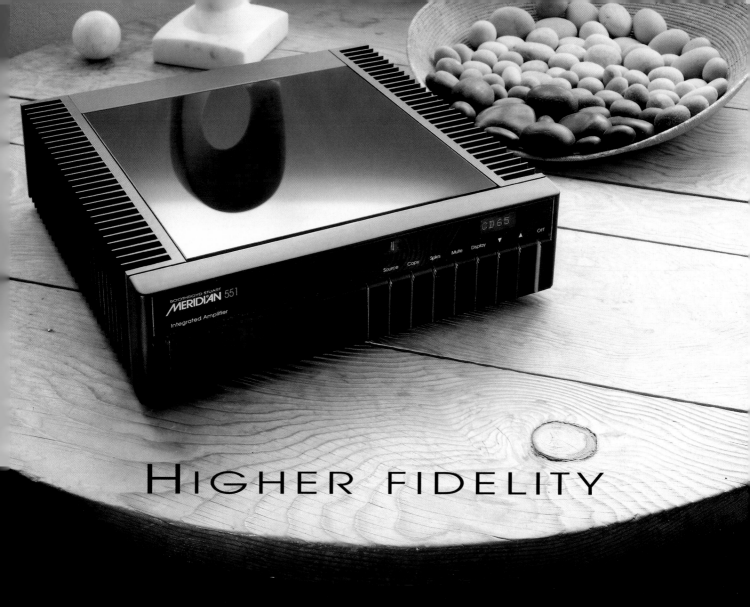

HIGHER FIDELITY

BOOTHROYD STUART
MERIDIAN©

Advanced video, digital and analogue Hi Fi systems. Send or call for our brochure and dealer list to
Meridian Audio Ltd 14 Clifton Road Huntingdon Cambridgeshire PE18 7EJ Tel 01480 52144

'DAWN CHORUS'. JAMES MARSH

TDK®

THE SPECIALISTS IN SOUND AND VISION.

Experience the Great Symphonies at the Barbican Centre this Autumn

Sir Simon Rattle's long awaited first Beethoven symphony cycle with the City of Birmingham Symphony Orchestra
(22 September - 27 October)

The Vaughan Williams symphonies performed by the Bournemouth Symphony Orchestra and Richard Hickox
(17 September - 9 October)

The complete Tchaikovsky symphony cycle with the St Petersburg Philharmonic Orchestra under Yuri Temirkanov
(15 - 18 October)

Other highlights include Great Orchestras of the World with the Oslo Philharmonic and London Symphony Orchestras and the Purcell Tercentenary weekend featuring Christopher Hogwood and The Academy of Ancient Music, The Sixteen and free foyer events.

BOX OFFICE: 0171 638 8891 *(9am - 8pm daily)* · BOOKING NOW OPEN

BBB Barbican Centre

The Barbican is owned funded and managed by the Corporation of London.

✂ Please send me details of Autumn events at the Barbican. There's no need for a stamp!

Name ——————————— Address ———————————

————————————— Daytime telephone number ———————————

PLEASE SEND TO: BARBICAN CENTRE MARKETING DEPT., FREEPOST LON 2089, LONDON EC2B 2QB

GET HINDEMITH

'AND GET with a capital G, g, e, t, GET Hindemith. Anyone who hasn't heard Hindemith play his own music has something to learn: about orchestration, about viola playing and about modern composition ... that can stand up to any work of the past asking no favours, but having its own organisation, as perfect as the organisation of woodfibres is in a tree trunk ... I am convinced that he stands peer to Stravinsky, as different as Bach is from Couperin.'

        – **Ezra Pound** *(1937)*

PAUL HINDEMITH INSTITUTE, FRANKFURT

1918

ORTY YEARS AGO, Paul Hindemith's position as one of the commanding figures of modern music – along with Bartók, Stravinsky and, if anything, somewhat ahead of that 'difficult' and controversial figure Arnold Schoenberg – looked assured. He was, quite simply, the most influential German composer of the twentieth century, and the most important since Richard Strauss. Yet the posthumous eclipse which seems to overtake, for a while, even the most eminent composers (Elgar and Sibelius are obvious examples) had in truth begun before his death in 1963, and it has proved unusually long-lasting. The centenary of his birth is surely time for an overdue reassessment.

But where to start? Our century has a problem knowing what value to place on sheer, magisterial artistic competence. How can we come to grips with a composer who had it in abundance, who composed abundantly, and in almost every conceivable form? A man who could play nearly every

'... and say bo! Kin your li'l friend Hindemith play the vi-olaaah? I'll say he can *play* the viola.'

        – **Ezra Pound**, *letter to Tibor Serly*

instrument, was a violin virtuoso in his teens, an acclaimed string quartet player, an internationally renowned violist and conductor; who made pioneering contributions to the revival of Early Music, who taught schoolchildren, well-established composers, and all grades between; who founded a musical academy in Turkey and thought deeply about the role, direction and meaning of music? A convivial, humorous man with apparently no skeletons in his cupboard, whose life to a great extent *was* music, Hindemith hardly appeals to the modern mode of biography, which regards artistic creation as a footnote to the failings and peccadillos of an artist's life, or suggests that true art arises only as a product of debauch or frustration.

The most dramatic episode in Hindemith's life came in the mid-1930s when, as Germany's leading non-Jewish contemporary composer, his music was denounced by the Nazi cultural machine and pilloried as an example of 'degenerate' art. The opera *Mathis der Maler*, his masterpiece, was denied a premiere on the German stage and performances of his other works were banned, in a move that closely paralleled the almost contemporary experience of Shostakovich in Stalin's Russia. Unlike Shostakovich, he was able to leave his native country; but he is sometimes criticised for taking so long about it.

Although he (or rather his publishers) did make attempts at a rapprochement with the régime, there is no question that Hindemith (whose wife was half-Jewish) was entirely anti-fascist in his beliefs. But as with many cultured Germans, simple patriotism and sheer incapacity to comprehend the political disaster that the Third Reich had unleashed on the nation delayed the final break. As it was, the *Mathis* affair focused the world's attention on him as a man of principle, and his exile in Switzerland and the USA (he never returned to live in Germany) served to increase his international reputation.

To some extent his subsequent critical devaluation was triggered by the rise in appreciation of the twentieth-century Viennese School (not so much Schoenberg, perhaps, as Mahler and Berg). Hindemith, who in later years set his face against many of the more radical developments of modern music, was too easily represented as an essentially conservative (and thus dispensable) figure. It was soon forgotten that he himself had participated in, and often instigated, many of those radical developments.

The received image of Hindemith is now largely coloured by the view that he was a mere academician, an over-productive craftsman strong on technique and scholastic *gravitas*, short on vision and sense of adventure, who produced – with admittedly staggering technique – yards of counterpoint, ubiquitous fourths-dominated harmony, a high-minded intricacy of discourse.

He suffers, that is to say, from the special problems that afflict composers with a highly characteristic, instantly recognisable style: you hear one work, you think you know them all. As a result it has recently been possible for Hindemith to be described as the most neglected of major twentieth-century composers.

And this, paradoxically, without the usual necessary precondition for neglect: the music's complete disappearance from common currency. It's a striking testimony to the solidity of Hindemith's achievement that his hold on some areas of repertoire seems as secure as ever, and if withdrawn would leave a gaping hole. Certain major pieces of his maturity – the ballet suite *Nobilissima Visione*, say, the *Mathis der Maler* Symphony, and of course the entertaining *Symphonic Metamorphoses on Themes of Weber* – have never relinquished their place in the concert hall. The vast majority of students and professional instrumentalists encounter Hindemith at some stage in their career, since he catered for all levels of musical attainment, and for virtually every

PAUL HINDEMITH INSTITUTE, FRANKFURT

Igor Stravinsky (seated, second from right) with members of the Amar Quartet, including Paul Hindemith (standing), 1924

HULTON DEUTSCH

1957

'one of the most defined and completely integrated styles of any composer now writing'
– **Aaron Copland**

Paul Hindemith

instrument – even those with tiny repertoires (where else can tuba or alto horn players go for their own sonatas?). To that extent his output pursues a certain life of its own, virtually immune to the vagaries of critical fashion.

In truth, Hindemith was very much a child of his time – one of that generation of confident, self-aware, sceptical artists who came to maturity just after the ravaging experience of the First World War: a generation with grave doubts about the nineteenth century's naive faith in progress, and the social imperialism and artistic gigantism to which that faith had given birth. The first young German composer to come to prominence after the War, Hindemith did so in the most controversial way, with a trilogy of one-act operas to Expressionist

super-refined orchestration in a tragic examination of sexual repression. *Susanna* retains its power to shock (an Italian production was denounced by the Vatican not so long ago) and wasn't heard in London until earlier this year. It reveals a composer capable of searing emotional expression.

Yet almost at once he threw himself into a very different series of works which synthesised jazz influences with the busy concerto-grosso style of the Baroque age: a vigorous, ironic, anti-Romantic music. Other composers soon followed that path: Kurt Weill, for instance, and (a name rapidly being revalued at the present time) Erwin Schulhoff. But to a large extent it was Hindemith who determined the German new-musical agenda, notably because he shaped the programmes and areas of interest at the influential chamber-music festivals in Donaueschingen and Baden-Baden throughout the 1920s, making that very much a decade of achievement in chamber genres, small ensembles, mechanical instruments, radio and film music – almost anything, in fact, rather than the overblown orchestral apparatus of the late-Romantic symphony and symphonic poem.

By the time of *Mathis der Maler*, however, Hindemith had come to question even the 'New Realism' of the 1920s. Conceived in the early months of the Hitler régime, the opera deals, precisely, with the role of the artist in times of political upheaval and moral chaos. He was putting his stylistic advances on a firm tonal and theoretical footing, and was contributing once more to the genres of opera, oratorio, symphony and concerto in their traditional amplitude and emotional intensity. In *Mathis*, and again in *Nobilissima Visione*, he drew sustenance from a vision of the Medieval world as an era of spiritual harmony.

This return to music's traditional functions of

Poster advertising Nazi exhibition of 'Degenerate Art', 1936

Right:
Design by L. Sievert for the premiere of Sancta Susanna, *Frankfurt, 1922*

AKG LONDON

PAUL HINDEMITH INSTITUTE, FRANKFURT

'... suggests the Medieval mating of ritual and ecstasy'
— *Glenn Gould*

texts that outraged conventional opinion with their frank approaches, from three different angles, to their common themes of unbridled sexual desire. In *Das Nusch-Nuschi* such subjects as adultery and castration are flippantly treated in glittering colours with irreverent quotations from Wagner; and in the fevered, hothouse atmosphere of the cloisters in *Sancta Susanna* he created his first masterpiece, handling all the latest resources of dissonance and

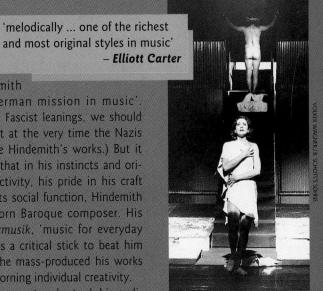

'melodically ... one of the richest and most original styles in music'
– *Elliott Carter*

tinues the article from which I quoted at the beginning by affirming that Hindemith 'has renewed the German mission in music'. (Remembering Pound's Fascist leanings, we should respect his writing that at the very time the Nazis were trying to expunge Hindemith's works.) But it would be truer to say that in his instincts and orientation, in his productivity, his pride in his craft and his awareness of its social function, Hindemith was essentially a reborn Baroque composer. His concept of *Gebrauchsmusik*, 'music for everyday use', was soon used as a critical stick to beat him with, suggesting that he mass-produced his works for the machine age, scorning individual creativity.

Yet of all the modern masters he took his audience least for granted, concerned at all times to maintain a human scale. What, after all, is his profoundly affecting *Trauermusik* ('Music of Mourning') for viola and strings – a memorial composed on the day of King George V's death, which Hindemith premiered with the BBC Symphony Orchestra the following evening – but an example of *Gebrauchsmusik* as it should be conceived: music for *every* day, effortlessly transcending its occasion and still moving us sixty years later?

A scene from the production of Sancta Susanna *at Trier in 1993*

romantic feeling, drama, protest and meditation, was already adumbrated in the stirring *Concert Music* for strings and brass he wrote for the Boston Symphony Orchestra's fiftieth anniversary – a work of symphonic breadth and scope; and the tendency reaches a climax in his turbulent works of the early years of World War II, such as the virtuosic Cello Concerto. With its wonderful slow-movement tune, this work confirms the primacy of melody in Hindemith's mature style.

It is possible that the area of his output which now most needs revaluation are those few, large, often darkly self-communing pieces of his last years, now so deeply out of fashion. Fashion, however, is precisely what Hindemith is *not* about. He is about the dignity, danger, delight and fleeting divinity of music-making from age to age. If we cannot 'get' that from him we miss the point entirely.

Ezra Pound – a surprising admirer, perhaps – con-

Top left: *Title-page of the vocal score of* Sancta Susanna

Right: *A page from Hindemith's piano work* Ludus Tonalis, *showing the composer's additional amendations*

"It's a John Cass"

This evening, as you applaud the conductor, the orchestra, and perhaps the composer, put your hands together for some other artists – those who shape the instruments which make the music.

It's a cherished art, instrument making. And nowhere is it more expertly taught than at London Guildhall University – the country's leading provider of music technology courses, offering degrees, HNDs and National Diplomas which cover everything from instrument making and servicing to musical electronic engineering.

Students come from all over the world to our legendary Sir John Cass Faculty of Arts, Design & Manufacture to make musical instruments and to carve a new future for themselves;

some of them could be contributing to tonight's performance.

You may not know their names, but do remember ours.

For further information contact (quoting ref PG):

Faculty Registry, Sir John Cass Faculty of Arts, Design & Manufacture, London Guildhall University, 41 Commercial Road, London E1 1LA.
Tel: +44 (0) 171-320 1827.

LONDON GUILDHALL
UNIVERSITY

ONE OF LIFE'S MORE REWARDING DECISIONS.

NOTES ON

'Sponge Relief', by Yves Klein (1928–62) TATE GALLERY, LONDON/BRIDGEMAN ART LIBRARY

PAINTING

Andrew Huth, introducing Prom 65, tells us how sight can become sound

SOONER OR LATER it occurs to most composers that painters have an easy life. The work involved in filling a canvas is nothing compared to the labour of writing out a full orchestral score, and when the painting is finished, there it is – over and done with, no need to copy parts, to entrust the music to singers and players, to rehearse against the clock, to suffer the agonies of a first performance and wonder if there will ever be a second … On reflection, though, and particularly when they consider that painters find it no easier to make a living than they do, composers generally come round to the idea that their own art does, after all, have its advantages. A painting doesn't actually *do* anything. It hangs on a wall without moving. It doesn't have a beginning, a middle and an end.

Nevertheless, many pieces of music have drawn their inspiration from painting and the other visual arts, and in Prom 65 four of these are combined in a programme given by the Junge Deutsche Philharmonie conducted by Markus Stenz: Rakhmaninov's *The Isle of the Dead*, Bernd Alois Zimmermann's *Photoptosis*, Liszt's *Totentanz* and Musorgsky's *Pictures at an Exhibition*.

How have these four very different composers set about creating parallels between sight and sound? Music cannot represent anything literally, but it has great powers of suggestion, and as soon as a composer gives an evocative title to a piece, our listening is inevitably conditioned by extra-musical associations. Two particular areas of musical technique, above all, have long been used to reinforce such suggestions: rhythm and colour.

However hard it might sometimes try, music cannot be still. Music *is* movement in time, so when a

composer wishes to recreate visual images in music, what is static has to become rhythmic. Pictures of people dancing or soldiers marching tell our eyes what is happening: music *becomes* the dance or the march. (It will of course be a fairly grim dance if the dancers happen to be skeletons, as in Liszt's *Totentanz*.)

Music can recreate the rhythms of nature which painting can only suggest by association. In *La Mer* Debussy famously evokes the movement of wind, light and water in a way that no other art could achieve. The rhythm of water is again the main element in Rakhmaninov's *The Isle of the Dead*. This was inspired by the painting by Arnold Böcklin (1827–1901) which the composer had admired in a Leipzig gallery. From the first notes the gloomy scene comes to life. The gently rocking rhythm conveys the lapping of water, and perhaps the slow movement of the mysterious boat with its Charon-like boatman, draped coffin and solitary mourner. A fluid orchestral texture, impregnated with the four-note *Dies irae* figure, rises eventually to a climactic, human protest, then finally returns to the lapping of the dark waters.

'Colour' in music is not an exact term, but a long-accepted metaphor (although for some composers, sound and colour really were the same: Rimsky-Korsakov, Skryabin and Messiaen all saw particular harmonies and chords as actual colours). We speak of the 'colour' of certain instruments, of 'dark' and 'bright' sounds. When a solo piano piece is rewritten for orchestra, the effect to our ears is similar to what our eyes perceive when a black and white sketch is coloured. Ravel's brilliant version of

Musorgsky's *Pictures at an Exhibition* is justly one of the most famous orchestrations in the repertory.

Since music is incapable of *literal* representation, perhaps it should be able to relate more easily to non-representational, abstract painting. The title of Bernd Alois Zimmermann's *Photoptosis* comprises the Greek words for 'light', 'seen' and 'falling away'. Zimmermann was fascinated by minute shadings of colour, and was particularly attracted to the work of the French painter Yves Klein (1928–62). The work was commissioned for the centenary in 1968 of the Bank of Gelsenkirchen in Germany, which owned a Klein painting; and Klein also contributed to the décor of the Gelsenkirchen Opera House, where he exploited a particular shade of ultramarine which he later patented (it's known as IKB – International Klein Blue).

The large orchestra of *Photoptosis*, including organ, is used to create a complex pattern of shifting musical colours which at one point is interrupted by a quotation from the opening to the finale of Beethoven's Ninth Symphony. This in turn leads

Portrait of Rakhmaninov by Boris Shalyapin (1940)

Bernd Alois Zimmermann

to a passage in which there appear fleeting references to the *Veni Creator* plainchant, Skryabin's *Poem of Ecstasy*, Wagner's *Parsifal*, Bach's First Brandenburg Concerto and Tchaikovsky's *Dance of the Sugar-Plum Fairy* – a series of 'representational' objects, as it were, which loom out from the background and fade away before the return of the shifting spectrum of 'abstract' orchestral colours.

Creating associations by quotation is an ancient practice which has been widely adopted in our own time. The *Dies irae* plainchant became a potent musical symbol of death in the Romantic period after its appearance in the finale of Berlioz's *Symphonie fantastique*. It is subtly woven into the texture of *The Isle of the Dead*, and emerges into flickering candle-lit glory in Liszt's *Totentanz* (Dance of Death) for piano and orchestra. This was apparently inspired by the fourteenth-century frescos of *The Last Judgment*, *Hell* and *The Triumph of Death* which he saw in the Camposanto at Pisa in 1838. In actual fact, Liszt's work has far more in common with a later artistic convention: it was only in the century following the Pisan frescos that the Dance of Death, showing skeletons leading all sorts and conditions of men to the grave, appeared for the first time in European iconography. Whatever the exact source of inspiration, the work is both evocative and exciting, displaying Liszt's romantic devilry at its most macabre as he revels in charnel-house acrobatics.

Among the most famous illustrations in music are Musorgsky's *Pictures at an Exhibition*. He wrote this piano suite in 1874 after an exhibition in memory of his artist friend Victor Hartmann, who had died the previous year. From this collection of architectural drawings, stage designs and watercolours, Musorgsky selected ten items for musical treatment. There is an extra dimension to the music – the presence of the composer himself, who can be heard moving from one exhibit to the next in the 'Promenade' which introduces and links the movements, the music varying according to his changing moods. These musical pictures

*Portrait of Musorgsky
by Ilya Repin (1881)*

Right: *'The Paris Catacombs',
by Hartmann, with the artist,
V. A. Kenel and a guide with
a lantern*

Below: *Victor Hartmann
(1834–73)*

Design for the Kiev City Gate, by Hartmann

are so famous and so vivid that it comes as something of a surprise to learn that only six of Hartmann's originals have survived, and we only have verbal descriptions of four of the works that inspired the composer. It seems a pity: but do we really need the pictures when we have Musorgsky's music?

The richness of musical language, and at the same time its very lack of precision, allow composers to bring paintings to life in a number of ways: and not only paintings. A glance though the programmes for this year's Proms shows us several works which use similar means to portray a rich gallery of human characters — legendary, like Strauss's Till Eulenspiegel, or real, like the friends Elgar depicted in his 'Enigma' Variations; and also to evoke the colour and movement of particular places, such as Respighi's Rome, Elgar's London or Mendelssohn's Italy and Scotland. For natural scenes, there are Debussy's sea, Strauss's Alps and the dark forest of Henze's Fourth Symphony.

Who would be a painter or a sculptor or a photographer or a film-maker, if they could be a composer instead?

Personal Insurance
in tune with your needs.

ZOE DOMINIC

Bernard Haitink

CLIVE BARDA / P.A.L.

Daniele Gatti

ALEX VON KOEFTLITZ

Mark Wigglesworth

CLIVE BARDA / P.A.L.

Sir Charles Mackerras

CLIVE BARDA / P.A.L.

Claudio Abbado

HANYA CHLALA

CLIVE BARDA / P.A.L.

Nikolaus Harnoncourt

GODFREY MACDOMNIC

Alexander Lazarev

MATTHEW FORD

Andrew Litton

ALEX VON KOEFTLITZ

Günter Wand

Libor Pešek

KATIE VANDYCK / P.A.L.

Yakov Kreizberg

PROMS 95

KATIE VANDYCK

Tadaaki Otaka

ALEX VON KOEFTLITZ

CLIVE BARDA / P.A.L.

Jane Glover

KATIE VANDYCK

Vernon Handley

Andrew Davis

GODFREY MACDOMNIC

Leonard Slatkin

ALEX VON KOEFTLITZ

Barry Wordsworth

HANYA CHLALA

Paul McCreesh

Ronald Corp

Martyn Brabbins

Sir Simon Rattle

Mark Elder

Robert King

Kent Nagano

Trevor Pinnock

CONDUCTORS

Claudio Abbado **31**
David Atherton **34**
Matthias Bamert **16**
Pierre Boulez **6**
Martyn Brabbins **22**
Riccardo Chailly **57, 58**
Ronald Corp **46**
Sir Peter Maxwell Davies **8**
Andrew Davis **1, 27, 38,
48, 66, 70**
Tan Dun* **24**
Mark Elder **21**
Peter Eötvös **56, 60**
Daniele Gatti* **3**
Jane Glover **55**
Bernard Haitink **20**
Vernon Handley **2**
Nikolaus Harnoncourt **25**
Richard Hickox **9**
Stephen Jackson* **15**
Mariss Jansons **28**
Neeme Järvi **63**
Simon Joly **69**
Robert King **12**
Oliver Knussen **17, 23**
Yakov Kreizberg **32**
Alexander Lazarev **11, 42**
Andrew Litton **54**
Paul McCreesh **67**
Sir Charles Mackerras **69**
Jerzy Maksymiuk **24**

Peter Mark* **45**
Marc Minkowski* **59**
Kent Nagano **14, 68**
Tadaaki Otaka **13, 61**
Libor Pešek **47**
Trevor Pinnock **29**
Sir Simon Rattle **10, 18**
Esa-Pekka Salonen **49**
Wolfgang Sawallisch* **43, 44**
Ulf Schirmer* **39**
En Shao* **30**
Leonard Slatkin **4**
Markus Stenz **33, 65**
Yan Pascal Tortelier **7, 8, 53**
Osmo Vänskä* **45**
Edo de Waart **50, 51**
Günter Wand **62**
Franz Welser-Möst **40**
Mark Wigglesworth **35, 52**
James Wood **64**
Barry Wordsworth **26, 36**

*Figures refer to Prom numbers
*First appearance at a
Henry Wood Promenade Concert*

En Shao

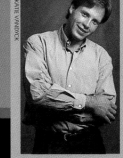

Markus Stenz

Yan Pascal Tortelier

Franz Welser-Möst

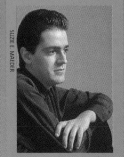

SUZIE E. MAEDER

Artur Pizarro

HANYA CHLALA

Colin Carr

CLIVE BARDA / P.A.L.

Katia and Marielle Labèque

KEITH SAUNDERS

Philip Dukes

Grigory Sokolov

CLIVE BARDA / P.A.L.

Håkan Hardenberger

ERICH HARTMANN / MAGNUM

Gidon Kremer

PETER MARES

Leon McCawley

SUZIE E. MAEDER

Dmitry Sitkovetsky

PROMS 95

HANYA CHLALA

Stephen Hough

JOHNNY GREIG

Rolf Hind

Jack Gibbons

CHRISTIAN STEINER

Heinrich Schiff

HANYA CHLALA

Tasmin Little

48

Kathryn Stott

Natalia Gutman

Yuri Bashmet

Thomas Zehetmair

Garrick Ohlsson

INSTRUMENTALISTS

Leif Ove Andsnes **4**
Andrew Antcliff* **42**
Andrew Ball* **64**
Yuri Bashmet **39**
Timothy Brown **42**
Colin Carr **2**
Paul Clarvis* **70**
Imogen Cooper **10**
James Crabb* **22**
Philip Dukes* **16**
Márta Fábián* **56**
Peter Frankl **56**
Jack Gibbons* **46**
Stephanie Gonley* **45**
Bruce Gremo* **24**
Natalia Gutman **63**
Clemens Hagen* **45**
Naji Hakim* **41**
Håkan Hardenberger **11**
John Harle **70**
Rolf Hind **65**
Stephen Hough **24**
Steven Isserlis **23**
Gidon Kremer **25, 49**
Kari Kriikku* **33**
Katia Labèque **3**
Marielle Labèque **3**
Christopher Larkin* **42**

John Lill **34**
Tasmin Little **70**
Leon McCawley* **54**
Wu Man* **19**
Venancio Mbande* **64**
Michael Murray* **42**
Garrick Ohlsson **53**
Ursula Oppens **40**
Boris Pergamenshikov* **11**
Maria João Pires **31**
Artur Pizarro **30**
Vadim Repin* **51**
Steven Schick* **64**
Heinrich Schiff **44**
Howard Shelley **26**
Dmitry Sitkovetsky **7**
Grigory Sokolov* **8**
Simon Standage **9**
Richard Stoltzman **36**
Kathryn Stott **45**
Jean-Yves Thibaudet **58**
Antje Weithaas **32**
Thomas Zehetmair **35**
Frank Peter Zimmermann **66**

Figures refer to Prom numbers
*First appearance at a
Henry Wood Promenade Concert

Imogen Cooper

Howard Shelley

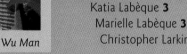

John Harle

Wu Man

49

Anne Sofie von Otter

Michael Chance

Randi Stene

Yvonne Kenny

Eva Randová

Siegfried Jerusalem

Joan Rodgers

Wolfgang Holzmair

Thomas Randle

James Bowman

Anthony Michaels-Moore

Nancy Argenta

Charlotte Margiono

Jane Henschel

Andreas Schmidt

Amanda Roocroft

Catherine Wyn-Rogers

Stephen Varcoe

PROM 95

50

SINGERS

Paul Agnew **29**
John Mark Ainsley **55**
Nancy Argenta **9, 29**
Melanie Armitstead **60**
Brian Bannatyne-Scott **29**
Kim Begley **1, 48**
Susan Bickley **23**
Ian Bostridge* **9**
James Bowman **12**
Victor Braun* **48**
Christine Brewer* **55**
Phyllis Bryn-Julson **6**
Susan Bullock* **53**
Connor Burrowes* **12**
Benjamin Butterfield* **59**
Michael Chance **9, 12**
Susan Chilcott* **63**
Paul Charles Clarke **61**
Rogers Covey-Crump **12**
Charles Daniels **12**
Menai Davies* **48**
Catherine Dubosc* **68**
Peter Evans* **29**
Jeannette Fischer* **68**
Michael George **12**
Susan Gorton* **48**
Susan Gritton **29**
Gunnar Gudbjörnsson* **60**
Stephen Guggenheim* **45**
Nancy Gustafson **52**
Alison Hagley **36**
Delphine Haidan* **68**
Robert Hale* **68**
Meredith Hall* **59**
Rosemary Hardy **17**
Markella Hatziano* **68**
Jane Henschel* **1**
Wolfgang Holzmair* **57**
Ann Howard **53**
Jason Howard* **49**
Judith Howarth **49**

Gwynne Howell **61**
Siegfried Jerusalem **27**
Amy Johnson* **45**
Della Jones **61**
Yvonne Kenny **1, 50**
Fiona Kimm **60**
Manuela Kriscak* **48**
Mikhail Krutikov **60**
François Le Roux **68**
Richard Lloyd-Morgan **29**
Jacques François Loiseleur
  des Longchamps* **59**
Linda Maguire* **59**
Rosa Mannion* **69**
Charlotte Margiono* **20**
David Mattinson* **63**
Donald Maxwell **26**
Anthony Michaels-Moore **1**
Douglas Nagel* **45**
Jard van Nes **21**
David Nickless **12**
Christiane Oelze **38**
Alan Opie **42**
Anne Sofie von Otter **27**
Hélène Perraguin* **68**
Brett Polegato* **59**
Dame Margaret Price **13**
Laura Pudwell* **59**
Thomas Randle **42**
Eva Randová **53**
Jean Rigby **1, 69**
Anthony Roden **48**
Joan Rodgers **16**
Amanda Roocroft **1**
Linda Russell **42**
Shari Saunders* **59**
René Schirrer **68**
Andreas Schmidt **55**
Michel Sénéchal **68**
Andrew Shore* **48**
Anja Silja **48**
Carsten Stabell* **1**
Randi Stene* **49**
Pamela Helen Stephen* **9**

Robert Tear **48**
John Tomlinson **52**
Julia Varady **1**
Stephen Varcoe **9, 12**
Christopher Ventris* **48**
Elisabeth Vidal* **68**
Janice Watson **61**
Lillian Watson **67**
Jeremy White **24**
David Wilson-Johnson **23**
Catherine Wyn-Rogers **42, 70**
Deborah York* **29**

*Figures refer to Prom numbers
*First appearance at a
Henry Wood Promenade Concert*

Nancy Gustafson

Dame Margaret Price

John Mark Ainsley

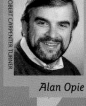
Christine Brewer

Jean Rigby

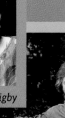
Julia Varady

John Tomlinson

Jason Howard

Alan Opie

Markella Hatziano

ARTISTS

305 entrants.
51 countries.
42 composers.
2 conductors.
52 strings.
18 brass.
16 woodwind.
25 competitors.
5 finalists.
7 judges.

1 sponsor.

All together now, it's the 1995 Cardiff Singer of the World Competition.

The five Concert Rounds and the Final are on BBC2 week commencing Monday 12th June.

All together better.

ORCHESTRAS & ENSEMBLES

Academy of Santa Cecilia* 3
BBC Concert Orchestra 2, 36
BBC National Orchestra of
  Wales 13, 34, 35, 61
BBC Philharmonic 7, 8, 53, 69
BBC Scottish Symphony
  Orchestra 22, 24, 45
BBC Symphony Orchestra
  1, 6, 11, 17, 23, 27, 32, 38,
  42, 49, 56, 62, 66, 70
Bournemouth Symphony
  Orchestra 54
Chamber Orchestra of Europe 25
City of Birmingham Symphony
  Orchestra 10, 18
Collegium Musicum 90* 9
Critical Band* 64
Danish Radio Symphony
  Orchestra 39
The English Concert 29
Ensemble Modern* 60
European Union Youth
  Orchestra 20
Gabrieli Players 67
Gustav Mahler Youth
  Orchestra 31

The Hague Percussion Group*
  64
Hallé Orchestra 14
The Hilliard Ensemble 5, 64
Julian Joseph All-Star Big Band*
  37
Junge Deutsche Philharmonie*
  65
The King's Consort 12
London Gabrieli Brass Ensemble
  15
London Mozart Players 16
The London Philharmonic 40, 48
London Sinfonietta 33
London Symphony Orchestra 68
Les Musiciens du Louvre* 59
Nash Ensemble 55
National Youth Orchestra of
  Great Britain 21
New London Orchestra 46
New Queen's Hall Orchestra* 26
Opera Atelier* 59
Oslo Philharmonic Orchestra 28
The Philadelphia Orchestra
  43, 44

Philharmonia Orchestra 4
The Premiere Ensemble* 52
Royal Concertgebouw
  Orchestra 57, 58
Royal Liverpool Philharmonic
  Orchestra 47
Royal Philharmonic Orchestra 55
Royal Scottish National
  Orchestra 63
Sydney Symphony Orchestra
  50, 51
Ulster Orchestra 30

CHOIRS

Bach Choir 55
BBC Singers 6, 17, 23, 27, 60,
  69, 70
BBC Symphony Chorus 1, 15,
  42, 49, 61, 70
BBC Welsh Chorus 61
Bournemouth Symphony
  Chorus 21
Brighton Festival Chorus 69
CBSO Chorus 1
Choir of Collegium

Musicum 90* 9
Choir of The English Concert 29
Choir of The King's Consort 12
Choir of New College, Oxford 12
Edinburgh Festival Chorus 69
Gabrieli Consort 67
The Glyndebourne Chorus 48
London Choral Society 55
London Philharmonic Choir 42
London Symphony Chorus 68
New London Children's Choir 68
Philharmonia Chorus 1
Polyphony* 5, 59
St Paul's Cathedral Choir* 1, 55
Boy and Girl Choristers of
  Salisbury Cathedral* 21
The Sixteen 53
Westminster Abbey Choir* 1
Westminster Cathedral Choir 1

MISCELLANEOUS

Fong Naam* 19
SamulNori* 19
Wu Man and Ensemble* 19

Figures refer to Prom numbers
*First appearance at
a Henry Wood Promenade
Concert

Julian Joseph

The Hilliard Ensemble

The English Concert

BBC Singers

BBC Scottish Symphony Orchestra

HOW TO BOOK

Full details of this year's Proms are given on page 61. There are three ways to book your tickets: either fill in the booking form, or from 5 June book by phone or in person.

By post

Postal booking for all concerts opens on **Thursday 11 May**. Ticket applications cannot be dealt with before this date. Please fill in the booking form on page 59 and post to:

Promenade Concerts Ticket Shop
Royal Albert Hall
London SW7 2AP

Please allow 28 days for delivery. A fee of £1.25 per booking will be added to cover postage and administration. Forms delivered by hand during the postal booking period do not receive priority.

By phone

From **Monday 5 June** you can book by phone on **0171-589 8212** between 9am and 9pm every day. A booking fee of £1.25 will be added to cover postage and administration.

In person

From **Monday 5 June** tickets will be on sale for personal bookings at the Royal Albert Hall Ticket Shop at Door 7, from 9am to 9pm daily.

Be warned! Some concerts may already be sold out by 5 June.

How to pay

Access, American Express and Visa are welcomed by the Royal Albert Hall. Just enter your credit card details in the box on the booking form.

Cheques and postal orders should be made payable to **Royal Albert Hall**. Ticket applications will be processed faster if the amount is left blank but with an upper limit stated; this avoids the need for refunds.

If the tickets you want are not available, lower-priced tickets for the same concert will be sent. Please tick the box on the booking form if this is NOT acceptable.

Tickets cannot be exchanged for other performances nor refunded except in the event of a cancelled performance.

Tickets for the Last Night

Subject to availability, one or two tickets per applicant will be allocated at the same price range to those who apply at the same time for the same number of tickets for at least five or more other concerts in the 1995 Proms season. If the Last Night is sold out, no refunds for other tickets purchased will be payable.

ALEX VON KOETLITZ

Car park booking

Car parking is only available for evening concerts and access is from 6pm. A limited number of car park spaces are available at Imperial College (entrance in Prince Consort Road) at £5.00, if you apply when booking your tickets. Just tick the column on the booking form.

Concert-goers with special needs

The Royal Albert Hall has up to 18 spaces for concert-goers in wheelchairs. Phone the Ticket Shop (0171-589 3203 ext 2670) to reserve.

An infra-red sound enhancement system is available for the hard of hearing. Receivers may be obtained free of charge from the Information Desk at Door 6.

Unaccompanied visually impaired concert-goers wishing to promenade in the Arena or Gallery should phone the Front of House Manager on 0171-589 3203 ext 2404 in advance.

Price Codes

	Stalls	Loggia Boxes 8 seats / 2nd Tier Boxes 4 seats	Choir	Balcony	Balcony Restricted View
A	£18.00	£14.50	£12.00	£9.00	£4.00
B	£22.00	£18.00	£15.00	£9.50	£4.00
C	£9.00	£9.00	£9.00	£6.50	£3.50
D	£12.00	£12.00	£10.00	£8.00	£3.50
E	£60.00	£60.00	£36.00	£36.00	£18.00

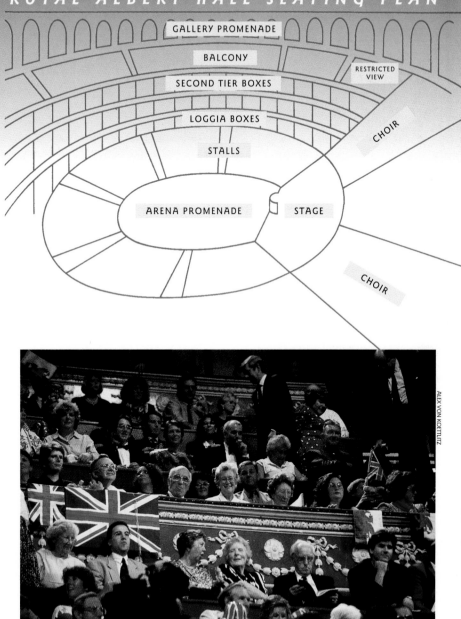

ROYAL ALBERT HALL SEATING PLAN

GALLERY PROMENADE
BALCONY
SECOND TIER BOXES
RESTRICTED VIEW
LOGGIA BOXES
CHOIR
STALLS
ARENA PROMENADE
STAGE
CHOIR

ALEX VON KOETTLITZ

HOW TO PROM

If you'd like to Prom this season and be at the centre of a unique musical experience, here's what to do.

Nightly tickets for the Arena and Gallery – the two standing areas – are available from Door 2 (Arena) and Door 10 (Gallery) one hour before the start of the concert. The queue often begins to form quite a bit earlier than this, and arrival one hour before the starting time will not always guarantee admission, especially to the Arena. Look for the signs for 'Arena Promenade Queue' or 'Gallery Promenade Queue'.

Promenade Tickets

(one per person, available at the door only – please have the correct money ready)

Arena	£3.00
Gallery	£2.00

If you'd like to come to the **Last Night**, tickets will be sold on a first-come, first-served basis if you've attended at least five other concerts. Please take your five ticket stubs to the Ticket Shop (Door 7) after you have been to your fifth Prom.

Season tickets

If you intend to Prom regularly, you can save money and guarantee admission by buying a season ticket. These are available for the Arena or the Gallery, and for the whole season, or the first or second half of the season. Season tickets are not transferable. To protect holders against loss and to prevent misuse, the Royal Albert Hall has requested those applying to enclose two passport photos with the completed booking form on page 59. A valid season ticket guarantees admission, provided you arrive not later than 10 minutes before the concert starts. As you'll already have a ticket, there's no need to queue, unless you want to be certain of your favourite place! You'll be let in one hour before the performance, through Door 11 (Arena) or Door 3 (Gallery).

Promenade Season Tickets

(one per person)

Arena *whole season*	£120.00
Arena *half season**	£75.00
Gallery *whole season*	£70.00
Gallery *half season**	£40.00

**1st half: 21 July – 18 August, plus Last Night*
2nd half: 19 August – 16 September

Free Pre-Prom Talks

There will be talks about aspects of the evening's music preceding many of this year's concerts. A full list can be found on page 104. Admission is free but space is limited, so please come early to avoid disappointment, as entry cannot be guaranteed (even for concert ticket holders). Doors open half an hour before the advertised start time of each talk, and there will be no admittance after the start.

Please note that the seating capacity in the Imperial College Students' Union Concert Hall is 300, and 470 in the Concert Hall of the Royal College of Music.

Free Education Events

A full listing of all the education events and performances can be found on page 113.

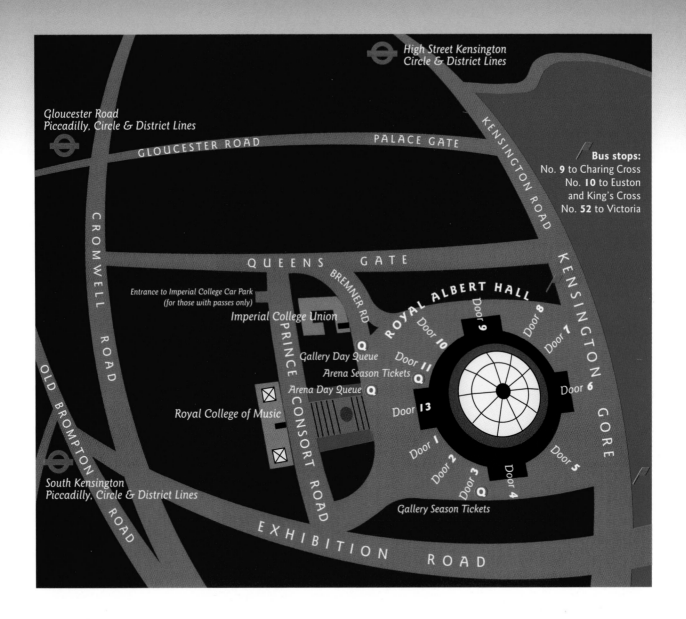

High Street Kensington
Circle & District Lines

Gloucester Road
Piccadilly, Circle & District Lines

GLOUCESTER ROAD

PALACE GATE

KENSINGTON ROAD

Bus stops:
No. **9** to Charing Cross
No. **10** to Euston
and King's Cross
No. **52** to Victoria

CROMWELL ROAD

QUEENS GATE

BREMNER RD

ROYAL ALBERT HALL

Entrance to Imperial College Car Park
(for those with passes only)

Imperial College Union

Door 10
Door 9
Door 8
Door 7

PRINCE CONSORT ROAD

Gallery Day Queue **Q**

Door II **Q**

Arena Season Tickets **Q**

Arena Day Queue **Q**

Door 6

OLD BROMPTON

Royal College of Music

Door **13**

KENSINGTON GORE

Door I

Door 2

Door 3

Door 4

Door 5

ROAD

South Kensington
Piccadilly, Circle & District Lines

Q

Gallery Season Tickets

EXHIBITION ROAD

INFORMATION

Information

An Information Desk is located in the Main Entrance Foyer (Door 6) to help you with your enquiries.

Doors open

Doors open three-quarters of an hour before each concert. On days when there are two concerts, there may be a slight delay in the opening of doors for the second concert. Latecomers will not be admitted into the hall unless or until there is a suitable break in the music.

Refreshments

Restaurants – the Elgar Room through Door 8 and the Victoria Room through Door 5 – are open from 5.30pm for dinner before each concert (reservations 0171-589 8900). A wine bar is situated in the Prince Consort Restaurant through Doors 13/14. For further details see the Ring and Brymer advertisement on page 85.

Bars are available on every floor and are open before the concert and during the interval. You can order interval drinks before the concert and bar staff will place your order on shelves around the bar. Please note that you are not permitted to bring your own food and drink for consumption in the Hall.

Privately owned seats

A high proportion of boxes as well as 600 stalls seats are privately owned. Unless returned by owners, these seats are not available for sale by the Ticket Shop.

Programmes

Nightly programmes are on sale at various locations round the hall. Promenaders may buy programmes at a reduced price in the Arena and Gallery.

Merchandise

A selection of BBC Proms merchandise will be on sale at Door 6 of the Royal Albert Hall two hours before evening concerts and one hour before afternoon concerts.

Inside the Hall

Please leave your hats and coats in the cloakroom at Door 4. Hand-luggage larger than a briefcase, food and drink, and folding chairs, are not allowed into the Hall. There is no smoking inside the auditorium, and cameras, tape-recorders and video cameras are not permitted. The Proms policy is that children under five are not allowed in the auditorium. The management reserves the right to refuse admission.

Broadcasting

All concerts are broadcast on BBC Radio 3 FM and some will be shown on BBC television. Please bear in mind the need for silence during the performance, and show consideration for the musicians, fellow concert-goers and listeners at home, by not coughing, and by turning off your watch alarms. Please do not bring mobile phones into the auditorium.

BOOKING FORM

Concert No.		Price code	No. of seats	Area	Car Parking	Total £	Office Use
1	Friday 21 July 8.00	B					
2	Saturday 22 July 7.30	A					
3	Sunday 23 July 7.30	A					
4	Monday 24 July 7.00	A					
5	Monday 24 July 10.00	C					
6	Tuesday 25 July 7.00	A					
7	Wednesday 26 July 7.30	A		SPECIAL OFFER!			
8	Thursday 27 July 7.00	A		SPECIAL OFFER!			
9	Thursday 27 July 10.00	C					
10	Friday 28 July 7.30	A					
11	Saturday 29 July 7.30	A					
12	Sunday 30 July 7.30	A					
13	Monday 31 July 7.30	A					
14	Tuesday 1 August 7.00	A					
15	Tuesday 1 August 10.00	C					
16	Wednesday 2 August 7.30	A					
17	Thursday 3 August 7.30	A		SPECIAL OFFER!			
18	Friday 4 August 7.00	A					
19	Friday 4 August 10.00	C					
20	Saturday 5 August 7.30	A					
21	Sunday 6 August 7.30	A					
22	Monday 7 August 7.00	A		SPECIAL OFFER!			
23	Monday 7 August 10.00	C					
24	Tuesday 8 August 7.00	A		SPECIAL OFFER!			
25	Wednesday 9 August 7.30	B					
26	Thursday 10 August 7.30	A					
27	Friday 11 August 7.30	A		SPECIAL OFFER!			
28	Saturday 12 August 7.30	B					
29	Sunday 13 August 7.30	A					
30	Monday 14 August 7.30	A					
31	Tuesday 15 August 7.30	B					
32	Wednesday 16 August 7.00	A					
33	Wednesday 16 August 10.00	C					
34	Thursday 17 August 7.30	A					
35	Friday 18 August 7.30	A					
36	Saturday 19 August 7.00	A		SPECIAL OFFER!			
37	Saturday 19 August 10.15	C					
38	Sunday 20 August 7.30	A					

Total carried forward

Complete this form (PLEASE USE BLOCK CAPITALS) and send it to:

Promenade Concerts Ticket Shop, Royal Albert Hall, London SW7 2AP

Indicate method of payment below.
DO NOT enclose s.a.e.
Bookings will include a £1.25 charge to cover postage and administration.

☐ Debit my (ACCESS/AMERICAN EXPRESS/VISA) card no.

☐☐☐☐☐☐☐☐☐☐☐☐☐☐☐☐☐☐

Expiry date   /

☐ I attach cheque/postal order made payable to Royal Albert Hall (please leave cheques open, with upper limit).

NAME _____

ADDRESS _____

_____

_____

_____

If you booked last year, please tick ☐
If you recall your Patron Number, please include it here ☐☐☐☐☐☐

TELEPHONE (day) _____
(evening) _____

SIGNATURE

_____

☐ **Do not** send lower priced tickets
☐ Special Offer Voucher(s) enclosed
☐ 2 passport photos enclosed
  (for season ticket applications only)

*not Restricted View or Prom

60

Concert No.		Price code	No. of seats	Area	Car Parking	Total £	Office Use
				Total brought forward			
39	Monday 21 August 7.30	A		SPECIAL OFFER!			
40	Tuesday 22 August 7.30	A					
41	Wednesday 23 August 6.00	C					
42	Wednesday 23 August 8.00	A					
43	Thursday 24 August 7.30	B					
44	Friday 25 August 7.30	B					
45	Saturday 26 August 7.30	A					
46	Sunday 27 August 11.30	A	*Full price for adults*			
				*Half price for under-14s**			
47	Sunday 27 August 8.00	A					
48	Monday 28 August 7.30	B					
49	Tuesday 29 August 7.30	A		SPECIAL OFFER!			
50	Wednesday 30 August 7.30	A					
51	Thursday 31 August 7.00	A					
52	Thursday 31 August 10.00	C					
53	Friday 1 September 7.30	A					
54	Saturday 2 September 7.30	A					
55	Sunday 3 September 7.30	A					
56	Monday 4 September 7.30	A		SPECIAL OFFER!			
57	Tuesday 5 September 7.30	B					
58	Wednesday 6 September 7.00	B					
59	Wednesday 6 September 10.00	D					
60	Thursday 7 September 7.00	A		SPECIAL OFFER!			
61	Friday 8 September 7.30	A					
62	Saturday 9 September 7.30	A					
63	Sunday 10 September 7.30	A					
64	Monday 11 September 7.30	A		SPECIAL OFFER!			
65	Tuesday 12 September 7.30	A					
66	Wednesday 13 September 7.00	A					
67	Wednesday 13 September 10.00	C					
68	Thursday 14 September 7.30	A					
69	Friday 15 September 7.30	A					
70	Saturday 16 September 7.30	E					
	Arena Season *whole season*			£120.00			
	half season			£75.00 *first half* ☐ *second half* ☐			
	Gallery Season *whole season*			£70.00			
	half season			£40.00 *first half* ☐ *second half* ☐			
					Total		

FRIDAY 21 JULY
8.00pm *ending at approximately 10.00pm*

Mahler
Symphony No. 8 in E flat major
'Symphony of a Thousand'

Part 1   26

INTERVAL

Part 2   60

Julia Varady *soprano*
Yvonne Kenny *soprano*
Amanda Roocroft *soprano*
Jane Henschel *mezzo-soprano*
Jean Rigby *mezzo-soprano*
Kim Begley *tenor*
Anthony Michaels-Moore *baritone*
Carsten Stabell *bass*

BBC Symphony Chorus
Philharmonia Chorus
CBSO Chorus
Choristers of St Paul's Cathedral,
Westminster Abbey and
Westminster Cathedral

BBC Symphony Orchestra
Andrew Davis *conductor*

The centenary celebrations of the world's
greatest music festival get off to a resounding
start with Mahler's 'Symphony of a Thousand'
as the first night of a season that includes a
complete cycle of Mahler's symphonies.

SATURDAY 22 JULY
7.30pm *ending at approximately 9.35pm*

Elgar orch. Gordon Jacob
Organ Sonata No. 1 in G major   24
Walton
Cello Concerto   29
INTERVAL
Vaughan Williams
Symphony No. 6 in E minor   34

Colin Carr *cello*

BBC Concert Orchestra
Vernon Handley *conductor*

The first Saturday of the season celebrates the
music of our own country. Vernon Handley's
fine Vaughan Williams performances and
recordings continue the great tradition of his
mentor, Sir Adrian Boult, who gave the premiere of the enigmatic Sixth Symphony in
1948, and two years earlier conducted the
first performance of Elgar's First Organ Sonata
(written 100 years ago) in the skilful orchestration by Gordon Jacob (also born in 1895).
Tonight's soloist made his Prom debut in
1981 in the Brahms Double Concerto,
returned four years later in the Elgar, and now
tackles Walton's concerto, written in 1956
for Gregor Piatigorsky.

SUNDAY 23 JULY
7.30pm *ending at approximately 9.40pm*

Respighi
Fountains of Rome   16
Poulenc
Concerto for Two Pianos   20
INTERVAL
Tchaikovsky
Symphony No. 6 in B minor
'Pathétique'   47

Katia and Marielle Labèque *pianos*

Academy of Santa Cecilia
Daniele Gatti *conductor*

The first of the season's visiting orchestras –
and indeed the first Italian symphony orchestra to play at the Proms – is another institu-
tion currently celebrating its centenary, the
Orchestra of the Accademia di Santa Cecilia
in Rome. The Academy itself dates back to
1566, numbering among its first members the
composers Palestrina and Marenzio, and in
1895 it formed an orchestra to give public
concerts. Its current conductor, Daniele Gatti
– who becomes Music Director of the Royal
Philharmonic Orchestra in 1996 – is now
enjoying a fully international career.
Respighi's most popular tone-poem and
Tchaikovsky's intensely personal symphony
enclose Poulenc's sparkling concerto, played
by the equally effervescent Labèque sisters.

Price code A

MONDAY 24 JULY

7.00pm *ending at approximately 9.10pm*

Hindemith
Concert Music for Brass and Strings,
Op. 50   18

Beethoven
Piano Concerto No. 2 in B flat major   29

INTERVAL

Elgar
Enigma Variations   34

Leif Ove Andsnes *piano*

Philharmonia Orchestra
Leonard Slatkin *conductor*

Purcell is not the only composer whose anniversary the BBC celebrates in 1995. In January a weekend festival at the Barbican was devoted to the music of Paul Hindemith, and four of his major works are played this season. The stunning young Norwegian pianist made his Prom debut three years ago in Britten's Piano Concerto, and now partners the Philharmonia, in its fiftieth-anniversary season, in Beethoven's Second – written exactly 200 years ago. Just before the performance of the 'Enigma', tonight's conductor (a staunch champion of Elgar's music) will give a ten-minute illustrated talk, offering his personal interpretation of the puzzle that has intrigued listeners for nearly a century.

Price code C

MONDAY 24 JULY

10.00pm *ending at approximately 11.15pm*

Arvo Pärt
St John Passion   70

The Hilliard Ensemble
Polyphony

The Hilliard Ensemble, who made such an impact at the 1990 Proms with their sensational performance of the *Miserere* by the Estonian composer Arvo Pärt, return with another major work by this European master. Like John Tavener, Pärt derives his inspiration from the plainchant and liturgy of the Russian Orthodox Church. The extraordinary popular success of his austere but serene music bears witness to a widespread desire to escape from the excesses of the secular world. His setting of the *St John Passion*, poised between the Lutheran and Catholic traditions, is performed with minimal forces – six solo singers, five players and chamber choir.

Price code A

TUESDAY 25 JULY

7.00pm *ending at approximately 9.50pm*

Pre-Prom Talk at 5.45pm
Pierre Boulez

Bartók
Music for Strings, Percussion
and Celesta   30

INTERVAL

Debussy
Jeux   18

Trois Ballades de Villon
Le Jet d'eau   16

Pierre Boulez
Le Soleil des eaux   10

INTERVAL

Messiaen
Et exspecto resurrectionem
mortuorum   31

Phyllis Bryn-Julson *soprano*

BBC Singers
BBC Symphony Orchestra
Pierre Boulez *conductor*

Boulez, who celebrated his seventieth birthday in March, takes up the baton of the BBC Symphony Orchestra once more in a typical programme of twentieth-century classics. American soprano Phyllis Bryn-Julson, one of the foremost interpreters of contemporary vocal music, has recorded *Le Soleil des eaux* with the composer. The programme opens with the first of this season's tributes to Bartók, who died in 1945.

WEDNESDAY 26 JULY

7.30pm *ending at approximately 9.35pm*

Pre-Prom Talk at 6.15pm
John Casken

Haydn
Symphony No. 83 in G minor
'The Hen'   23

John Casken
Violin Concerto   c30
BBC commission: world premiere

INTERVAL

Stravinsky
Petrushka (1911)   33

Dmitry Sitkovetsky *violin*
BBC Philharmonic
Yan Pascal Tortelier *conductor*

Together with its Principal Conductor, Yan Pascal Tortelier, the BBC Philharmonic has achieved outstanding success over the past few years in an ever-widening range of repertoire. This lively programme opens with Haydn's popular symphony, one of a set he wrote for performance in Paris in 1785, and closes with the original version of Stravinsky's colourful ballet score. In between, the brilliant Russian violinist gives the world premiere of the first of this season's BBC Proms commissions, discussed by Adrian Jack on page 88.

THURSDAY 27 JULY

7.00pm *ending at approximately 9.10pm*

Pre-Prom Talk at 5.45pm
Sir Peter Maxwell Davies

Elgar
Overture 'Cockaigne'   15
Sir Peter Maxwell Davies
The Beltane Fire*   35
BBC commission: European premiere

INTERVAL

Rakhmaninov
Piano Concerto No. 3 in D minor   42

Grigory Sokolov *piano*
BBC Philharmonic
Yan Pascal Tortelier *conductor*
Sir Peter Maxwell Davies *conductor**

Another major new commission forms the centrepiece of the BBC Philharmonic's second programme. *The Beltane Fire* received its world premiere in the USA in April on the orchestra's American tour, part of its current sixtieth-anniversary season. Two popular favourites complete the programme: Elgar's lively evocation of Edwardian London, and Rakhmaninov's much-loved concerto, the work in which the Russian pianist Grigory Sokolov – a former Tchaikovsky Competition winner, and now internationally acclaimed as an artist of the first rank – made his UK debut at the 1990 Edinburgh Festival.

THURSDAY 27 JULY

10.00pm *ending at approximately 11.20pm*

Bach
Sinfonia from Cantata No. 42   7
Singet dem Herrn   13
Violin Concerto in A minor   14
Magnificat in D major   26

Simon Standage *violin*

Nancy Argenta *soprano*
Pamela Helen Stephen *soprano*
Michael Chance *counter-tenor*
Ian Bostridge *tenor*
Stephen Varcoe *baritone*

Collegium Musicum 90 Choir
and Orchestra
Richard Hickox *conductor*

A relative newcomer to the period-instrument scene, the Collegium Musicum 90 Choir and Orchestra, formed by conductor Richard Hickox and leader Simon Standage in 1990 to give historically-accurate performances of familiar and less well-known repertoire, makes its Prom debut tonight. The group has already issued over twenty CDs, including the Bach B minor Mass.

Price code A
FRIDAY 28 JULY

7.30pm *ending at approximately 10.00pm*

10

Mozart
Piano Concerto No. 18
in B flat major, K456   30

INTERVAL

Mahler
Symphony No. 6 in A minor   85

Imogen Cooper *piano*

City of Birmingham Symphony Orchestra
Sir Simon Rattle *conductor*

Imogen Cooper – one of Britain's best-loved
pianists and always a great favourite with
Prom audiences – recently made her debut
with the Berlin Philharmonic Orchestra under
Sir Simon Rattle, whom she partners once
more in the elegant concerto Mozart wrote
for the blind virtuoso Maria Theresia von
Paradis. Sir Simon is having a typically hectic
season, with 'Towards the Millennium' concerts in London and Birmingham, a major
European tour with the CBSO, and appearance in a Mahler cycle in Brussels and
Amsterdam in which he is working with the
Vienna Philharmonic. Paul Banks writes about
Mahler's ascendancy on page 22.

Price code A
SATURDAY 29 JULY

7.30pm *ending at approximately 9.45pm*

11

Rimsky-Korsakov
The Golden Cockerel – suite   30

Tchaikovsky
Variations on a Rococo Theme   18

INTERVAL

Sir Harrison Birtwistle
Endless Parade   18

Shostakovich
Symphony No. 6 in B minor   31

Boris Pergamenshikov *cello*

Håkan Hardenberger *trumpet*

BBC Symphony Orchestra
Alexander Lazarev *conductor*

The BBC Symphony's Principal Guest
Conductor introduces another Tchaikovsky
Competition first prizewinner to the Proms in
Tchaikovsky's charming variations. Rimsky-
Korsakov's posthumously produced parody of
a Pushkin folk-story achieved Western popu-
larity through Dyagilev's spectacular 1914
Paris production for the Russian Ballet.
Birtwistle's variation-form processional was
commissioned by Paul Sacher for the brilliant
young Swedish trumpeter.

Price code A
SUNDAY 30 JULY

7.30pm *ending at approximately 9.40pm*

12

Purcell
My Heart is Inditing   16

Jeremiah Clarke
Come, come along   24

Purcell
Hear my Prayer   3

INTERVAL

Blow
Ode on the Death of
Mr Henry Purcell   20

Purcell
Remember not, Lord, our offences   3

Funeral Music for Queen Mary   20

Connor Burrowes *treble*
David Nickless *treble*
James Bowman *counter-tenor*
Michael Chance *counter-tenor*
Rogers Covey-Crump *tenor*
Charles Daniels *tenor*
Stephen Varcoe *baritone*
Michael George *bass*

Choir of New College, Oxford
Choir of The King's Consort
The King's Consort
Robert King *conductor*

A commemoration of Purcell's death, with a
mixture of funeral music by him and works by
fellow-composers mourning his loss.

MONDAY 31 JULY

7.30pm *ending at approximately 9.40pm*

Mendelssohn
Symphony No. 4 in A 'Italian' 27

Verdi
Willow Song and Ave Maria
from 'Otello' 14

INTERVAL

Ravel
Shéhérazade 17

Lutoslawski
Symphony No. 3 30

Dame Margaret Price *soprano*
BBC National Orchestra of Wales
Tadaaki Otaka *conductor*

In the seven years since Tadaaki Otaka's appointment the BBC National Orchestra of Wales has flourished, with concerts, broadcasts, several outstandingly successful foreign tours, and a burgeoning discography which consistently attracts glowing critical praise. Lutoslawski's Third Symphony, written for the Chicago Symphony Orchestra in 1983, shows their adventurous programming and high-calibre playing. In the first of its four visits to this year's Proms, the orchestra is joined by one of Wales's most internationally celebrated singers.

TUESDAY 1 AUGUST

7.00pm *ending at approximately 9.15pm*

Pre-Prom Talk at 5.45pm
Thomas Adès
and Judith Bingham

Webern
Six Pieces for Orchestra, Op. 6 12

Thomas Adès
... but all shall be well 11
London premiere

INTERVAL

Mahler
Symphony No. 5 75

Hallé Orchestra
Kent Nagano *conductor*

1945 marked the death not only of Bartók, but also of Anton Webern, accidentally shot by an American soldier a few yards from his home. Under its brilliant American conductor, the Hallé also tackles one of the most popular of Mahler's symphonies, its exquisite Adagietto an expression of the composer's love for his future wife, and a new work by its twenty-three-year-old Composer-in-Residence. Thomas Adès describes his first orchestral score, premiered in March of last year, as 'a consolation for orchestra, an almost entirely melodic piece', though its message, he says, is ambiguous.

TUESDAY 1 AUGUST

10.00pm *ending at approximately 11.20pm*

Giovanni Gabrieli
Buccinate in neomenia tuba 4
Canzona (No. 15) a 12, from
'Sacrae Symphoniae', 1597 4

Ives
Psalm 67 3
Psalm 90 10

Judith Bingham
Salt in the Blood c20
BBC commission: world premiere

Ives
Three Harvest Home Chorales 10

Giovanni Gabrieli
Canzona (No. 18) a 14, from
'Symphoniae Sacrae', 1615 5
Omnes gentes 4

BBC Symphony Chorus
London Gabrieli Brass Ensemble
Stephen Jackson *conductor*

The BBC's large amateur choir offers a selection of pieces for choir and brass under its director Stephen Jackson. Polychoral motets from seventeenth-century Venice are contrasted with works by that great American original Charles Ives – two double-choir psalm settings, and a set of *Three Harvest Home Chorales* thought to date from 1898. You can read about Judith Bingham's 'ghost story at sea' on page 88.

WEDNESDAY 2 AUGUST

7.30pm *ending at approximately 9.50pm*

Pre-Prom Talk at 6.15pm
Sally Beamish

Mozart
Eine kleine Nachtmusik 16

Sally Beamish
Viola Concerto 20
world premiere

INTERVAL

Mozart
Serenata notturna 11

Britten
Les Illuminations 23

Mozart
Symphony No. 39
in E flat major, K543 29

Philip Dukes *viola*
Joan Rodgers *soprano*

London Mozart Players
Matthias Bamert *conductor*

Matthias Bamert has been Music Director of the London Mozart Players since 1992, but this is their first Prom together. Mozart's *A Little Night Music*, apparently written as light relief while he was working intensively on *Don Giovanni*, has always been one of his most popular works. It is complemented by the great E flat symphony, completed a year later, in 1788. Joan Rodgers, who has starred in so many Mozartian roles, sings Britten's translucently-scored Rimbaud song-cycle.

THURSDAY 3 AUGUST

7.30pm *ending at approximately 9.30pm*

Pre-Prom Talk at 6.15pm
Oliver Knussen

Mahler
Todtenfeier 26

Oliver Knussen
Chiara c15
BBC commission: world premiere

INTERVAL

Mahler arr. Britten
What the Wild Flowers Tell Me 10

Hans Werner Henze
Symphony No. 4 24

Rosemary Hardy *soprano*

BBC Singers
BBC Symphony Orchestra
Oliver Knussen *conductor*

A new piece by Oliver Knussen is always an eagerly-anticipated event, and Rosemary Hardy – who sang the part of Max in the Glyndebourne production of *Where the Wild Things Are* – is one of Knussen's finest vocal interpreters. *Chiara* is framed by two Mahler 'offcuts', the first, *Funeral Rites*, an early incarnation of what was to become the first movement of the Second Symphony, and the second, from the Third Symphony, re-orchestrated in 1941 by Britten. Henze's lyrical Fourth Symphony was originally conceived as the finale to Act 2 of his evocative, fairy-tale opera *King Stag* (1953–5).

SPECIAL OFFER!

FRIDAY 4 AUGUST

7.00pm *ending at approximately 9.05pm*

Pre-Prom Talk at 5.45pm
Hans Werner Henze

NOTE TIME

Mendelssohn
Overture 'A Midsummer
Night's Dream' 12

Hans Werner Henze
Symphony No. 8 26
UK premiere

INTERVAL

Beethoven
Symphony No. 3 in E flat major
'Eroica' 50

City of Birmingham Symphony Orchestra
Sir Simon Rattle *conductor*

Another symphony by Henze forms the centrepiece of this programme conducted by Sir Simon Rattle, one of the composer's most eloquent British advocates, who introduced the Seventh Symphony to the UK at the 1986 Proms, and later recorded it. The Eighth, written for the Boston Symphony and first performed in the USA two years ago, continues Henze's preoccupation with the world of fantasy. In this case its inspiration was drawn directly from *A Midsummer Night's Dream*, and the work is appropriately prefaced by Mendelssohn's entrancing overture to Shakespeare's play.

FRIDAY 4 AUGUST
10.00pm *ending at approximately 1.15am*

Music from the Far East
SamulNori
(Korea)   45
Wu Man and Ensemble
(China)   45
INTERVAL
Fong Naam
(Thailand)   60

This spectacular Prom features the highly individual timbres and colours of three different ensembles from the Far East. Korea's foremost drum and dance ensemble has achieved worldwide success by recreating traditional genres as dynamic entertainment with powerful audience appeal. Wu Man, who has played, broadcast and recorded throughout the world, is one of China's leading players of both traditional and contemporary music. In tonight's concert she is accompanied by colleagues playing a wide variety of traditional Chinese instruments. Fong Naam, an ensemble of the finest Thai musicians founded by American scholar and performer Bruce Gaston and the brilliant soprano xylophonist Boonyong Ketkhong, aims to maintain the venerable tradition of Thai classical music.

SATURDAY 5 AUGUST
7.30pm *ending at approximately 9.30pm*

Strauss
Death and Transfiguration   23
Four Last Songs   21
INTERVAL
Stravinsky
The Rite of Spring   33

Charlotte Margiono *soprano*
European Union Youth Orchestra
Bernard Haitink *conductor*

Last year Bernard Haitink was appointed Music Director of the magnificent European Union Youth Orchestra, whose visits to the Proms have been so spectacularly successful. This year they have chosen to couple two of Strauss's most transcendental works with Stravinsky's intensely exciting but rather more brutal vision of extinction – the sacrifice of a pagan virgin to appease the gods of fertility. The brilliant young Dutch soprano Charlotte Margiono, who last year made a stunningly successful debut as Desdemona with the Brussels Opera, and toured Europe with the EUYO, makes her debut in Strauss's glorious swansong. Here, shortly before his own death, he quoted from his tone-poem *Death and Transfiguration*, composed sixty years before.

SUNDAY 6 AUGUST
7.30pm *ending at approximately 9.15pm*

Mahler
Symphony No. 3 in D minor   95

Jard van Nes *mezzo-soprano*

Boy and Girl Choristers of
Salisbury Cathedral
Bournemouth Symphony Chorus
women's voices
National Youth Orchestra of Great Britain
Mark Elder *conductor*

Another top-rank Dutch singer, who has won critical plaudits all over the world for her Mahler interpretations, joins Mark Elder and our own National Youth Orchestra in a symphony whose grandeur and dramatic sweep were inspired by Mahler's intense love of nature. The NYO always selects the most testing repertoire for its annual Prom appearances, and this great work will provide a formidable challenge.

MONDAY 7 AUGUST

7.00pm *ending at approximately 9.10pm*

Pre-Prom Talk at 5.45pm
Lyell Cresswell and James Crabb

Ravel
Alborada del gracioso 7

Lyell Cresswell
Dragspil c20
BBC commission: world premiere

Debussy
Ibéria from 'Images' 20

INTERVAL

Dvořák
Symphony No. 8 in G major 40

James Crabb *accordion*

BBC Scottish Symphony Orchestra
Martyn Brabbins *conductor*

The accordion is currently gaining credibility as a solo instrument, and virtuoso James Crabb has been hailed as one of its finest exponents. Born in New Zealand, Lyell Cresswell now lives in Scotland, where he is one of several composers to benefit from the innovative commissioning policy of the BBC Scottish Symphony Orchestra, which celebrates its sixtieth anniversary this year. The spirit of place – Spain and Bohemia – informs the rest of this colourful programme, directed by the orchestra's Associate Conductor.

SPECIAL OFFER!

MONDAY 7 AUGUST

10.00pm *ending at approximately 11.25pm*

Stravinsky
The King of the Stars 6

Three Russian sacred choruses: 7
  Otche nash'
  Bogoroditse devo
  Simvol' verï

John Tavener
The Protecting Veil 43

Stravinsky
Requiem Canticles 14

Steven Isserlis *cello*

Susan Bickley *mezzo-soprano*
David Wilson-Johnson *baritone*

BBC Singers
BBC Symphony Orchestra
Oliver Knussen *conductor*

Scored for chorus and vast orchestra, Stravinsky's *The King of the Stars* (1912) was dedicated to Debussy, who wrote that he could not foresee performances of this extraordinary 'planetary cantata' – 'except on Sirius or Aldebaran'. Stravinsky's three individual settings of Slavonic texts are middle-period works, while his 'pocket Requiem' was one of his very last compositions, dating from 1965–6. John Tavener's 1989 BBC commission has achieved massive popular success in the recording by Steven Isserlis, who premiered it at the Proms under tonight's conductor.

TUESDAY 8 AUGUST

7.00pm *ending at approximately 10.00pm*

Pre-Prom Talk at 5.45pm
Tan Dun

Tchaikovsky
Romeo and Juliet 17

Rakhmaninov
Rhapsody on a Theme of Paganini 24

INTERVAL

Tan Dun
Orchestral Theatre I: Xun* 20
London premiere

Orchestral Theatre II: Re* 22
UK premiere

INTERVAL

Shostakovich
Symphony No. 9 in E flat major 26

Stephen Hough *piano*
Bruce Gremo *xun*
Jeremy White *bass*

BBC Scottish Symphony Orchestra
Jerzy Maksymiuk *conductor*
and Tan Dun *conductor**

Tan Dun, who currently lives in New York, has achieved startling success in the USA, the Far East and Europe. A disciple of John Cage, he draws inspiration from silence and natural sounds. At the heart of this programme are two works which he describes as 'Orchestral Theatre' – one featuring the ceramic wind instrument called a 'xun', the other in which the composer will invite the audience to participate by chanting.

Price code B

WEDNESDAY 9 AUGUST

7.30pm *ending at approximately 9.35pm*

25

Mendelssohn
Overture 'The Hebrides'   10
Schumann
Violin Concerto in D minor   33
INTERVAL
Mendelssohn
Overture 'The Fair Melusine'   11
Schubert
Symphony No. 4 in C minor 'Tragic'   31

Gidon Kremer *violin*

Chamber Orchestra of Europe
Nikolaus Harnoncourt *conductor*

Nikolaus Harnoncourt returns to the Proms with a marvellous orchestra, a world-famous violinist and an early Romantic programme. Two watery overtures by Mendelssohn, one the famous depiction of his stormy boat journey in August 1829 to Fingal's Cave on the Scottish island of Staffa, the other inspired by the legend of the mermaid Melusine, frame Schumann's concerto, written towards the end of his life for the twenty-two-year-old Joseph Joachim, which nevertheless lay unperformed until 1937.

Price code A

THURSDAY 10 AUGUST

7.30pm *ending at approximately 9.55pm*

Pre-Prom Talk at 6.15pm
John Drummond

26

100th Anniversary of the First Promenade Concert
Wagner
Overture 'Rienzi'   12
Leoncavallo
Prologue to 'Pagliacci'   6
Mendelssohn
Piano Concerto No. 1 in G minor   20
INTERVAL
Thomas
Overture 'Mignon'   8
Schubert
Symphony No. 8 in B minor
'Unfinished'   25
Rossini
'Largo al factotum' from
'The Barber of Seville'   4
Bizet
Carmen – Suite No. 1   11

Donald Maxwell *baritone*
Howard Shelley *piano*

New Queen's Hall Orchestra
Barry Wordsworth *conductor*

Tonight marks the 100th anniversary of the very first Prom. The programme was extremely long, so this partial reconstruction concentrates on highlights: five items from the opening night, plus the first concerto and symphony to be played in the series.

Price code A

FRIDAY 11 AUGUST

7.30pm *ending at approximately 9.40pm*

Pre-Prom Talk at 6.15pm
Judith Weir

27

Webern
Passacaglia, Op. 1   10
Judith Weir
Moon and Star   c20
BBC commission: world premiere
INTERVAL
Mahler
Das Lied von der Erde   63

Anne Sofie von Otter *mezzo-soprano*
Siegfried Jerusalem *tenor*

BBC Singers
BBC Symphony Orchestra
Andrew Davis *conductor*

Webern's first masterpiece and a new work by one of Britain's most acclaimed composers precede Mahler's exquisite symphonic song-cycle, in which the BBC Symphony Orchestra and its Chief Conductor are joined by two of the finest singers of our time, the great Wagnerian tenor Siegfried Jerusalem, and Anne Sofie von Otter, whose voice has proved particularly well-suited to the late-Romantic repertoire.

SPECIAL OFFER!

SATURDAY 12 AUGUST

7.30pm *ending at approximately 9.35pm*

Pre-Prom Talk at 6.15pm
Mariss Jansons

Magnar Åm
Study on a Norwegian Hymn   9
UK premiere

Strauss
Also sprach Zarathustra   34

INTERVAL

Sibelius
Symphony No. 2 in D major   43

Oslo Philharmonic Orchestra
Mariss Jansons *conductor*

The Oslo Philharmonic Orchestra is always a welcome visitor to the Proms. Magnar Åm was born in Norway in 1952, and studied with Ingvar Lidholm in Stockholm. His 1976 Study, based on a local tune which the composer discovered himself, was composed for organ, then recomposed for full orchestra. Strauss's Nietzschean tone-poem provides an occasionally ironic commentary on the German philosopher's controversial doctrine of the 'Superman', while Sibelius's most overtly nationalistic symphony is shot through with luscious melody.

SUNDAY 13 AUGUST

7.30pm *ending at approximately 9.55pm*

Purcell
King Arthur

Part I   62

INTERVAL

Part II   46

Nancy Argenta *soprano*
Susan Gritton *soprano*
Deborah York *soprano*
Paul Agnew *tenor*
Peter Evans *tenor*
Brian Bannatyne-Scott *bass*
Richard Lloyd-Morgan *bass*

Choir of The English Concert
The English Concert
Trevor Pinnock *conductor*

Trevor Pinnock takes up the baton for this concert adaptation of Purcell's semi-opera *King Arthur*, first heard at London's Dorset Garden Theatre 304 years ago. This performance uses Louis MacNeice's narration, a paraphrase of Dryden's text originally written for a radio production. Two young British sopranos, both shooting rapidly to fame, join Canadian Nancy Argenta in the solo line-up. Susan Gritton made her Prom debut two years ago in Handel's *Deborah*, and has since recorded many of Purcell songs.

MONDAY 14 AUGUST

7.30pm *ending at approximately 9.45pm*

Pre-Prom Talk at 6.15pm
Michael Torke

Michael Torke
Green   12

Skryabin
Piano Concerto in F sharp minor   28

INTERVAL

Shostakovich
Symphony No. 10 in E minor   52

Artur Pizarro *piano*
Ulster Orchestra
En Shao *conductor*

The Ulster Orchestra makes its first visit to the Proms under its new Principal Conductor. Originally entitled *Verdant Music*, the 1986 score by the American post-minimalist 'suggests a quality that is simple and unseasoned ... it reflects the values of the people of Wisconsin' (where Torke comes from). Artur Pizarro won the hearts of the British public with his well-deserved win at the 1990 Leeds International Piano Competition. Here he plays the rarely-heard concerto by Alexander Skryabin, a high watermark of late-Romanticism dating from 1898.

TUESDAY 15 AUGUST

7.30pm *ending at approximately 9.35pm*

31

Beethoven
Piano Concerto No. 3 in C minor   34

INTERVAL

Bruckner
Symphony No. 9 in D minor   55

Maria João Pires *piano*

Gustav Mahler Youth Orchestra
Claudio Abbado *conductor*

The Gustav Mahler Youth Orchestra, which has done so much to unite young musicians from Eastern and Western Europe, returns for its third visit to the Proms under its Principal Conductor. Two seasons ago the orchestra gave an unforgettable performance of Bruckner's Fifth. Now it moves on to the Ninth, begun in 1889 but left incomplete at the composer's death seven years later. The Portuguese virtuoso pianist is a former winner of the Beethoven Competition in Brussels, and her recordings include all the Mozart sonatas. Here she plays the Third Piano Concerto of Bruckner's idol.

WEDNESDAY 16 AUGUST

7.00pm *ending at approximately 9.05pm*

32

Musorgsky arr. Rimsky-Korsakov
A Night on the Bare Mountain   10

Shostakovich
Violin Concerto No. 1 in A minor   36

INTERVAL

Bartók
Concerto for Orchestra   38

Antje Weithaas *violin*

BBC Symphony Orchestra
Yakov Kreizberg *conductor*

Yakov Kreizberg, recently appointed Principal Conductor of the Bournemouth Symphony Orchestra, conducts this Eastern European programme. The young soloist plays Shostakovich's First Violin Concerto, written at the time of the Stalinist crackdown in 1947–8, then withdrawn and reworked for its 1955 premiere. Before it comes Musorgsky's heady witches' brew, describing a diabolical orgy held on St John's Night on the Bare Mountain, while the fiftieth anniversary of Bartók's death is commemorated with a performance of his most popular orchestral work.

WEDNESDAY 16 AUGUST

10.00pm *ending at approximately 11.20pm*

33

György Ligeti
Melodien   12

Benedict Mason
Clarinet Concerto   20
BBC commission: world premiere

Conlon Nancarrow arr. Mikhashoff
Studies for Player Piano   8

Varèse
Octandre   8

Julian Anderson
Khorovod   12

Kari Kriikku *clarinet*

London Sinfonietta
Markus Stenz *conductor*

Two twentieth-century classics are interwoven with new pieces by two of Britain's brightest younger composers. Julian Anderson's *Khorovod*, a London Sinfonietta commission, was premiered under Markus Stenz, the orchestra's Principal Conductor, last December. Its title means 'Round Dance', and the composer says it's a joyous celebration that draws on Russian folk music. On page 88 Adrian Jack talks about Benedict Mason, whose concerto is a joint BBC/Helsinki Festival commission.

Price code A

THURSDAY 17 AUGUST

7.30pm *ending at approximately 9.40pm*

34

Messiaen
Un Sourire 7

Prokofiev
Piano Concerto No. 3 in C major 29

INTERVAL

Berlioz
Symphonie fantastique 55

John Lill *piano*

BBC National Orchestra of Wales
David Atherton *conductor*

David Atherton, currently Principal Guest Conductor of the BBC National Orchestra of Wales, has been showered with international recording awards. In 1992 he marked his twenty-fifth Prom season with Berlioz's *The Childhood of Christ*, and now returns with one of the most exciting of all Romantic symphonies. John Lill's performance of Prokofiev's effervescent concerto is prefaced by Messiaen's bicentennial tribute to Mozart, of which the composer wrote: 'Despite bereavements, sufferings, hunger, cold, incomprehension and the proximity of death, Mozart still smiled, his music too. That is why I allowed myself, in all humility, to call my act of homage "A Smile"'.

Price code A

FRIDAY 18 AUGUST

7.30pm *ending at approximately 9.45pm*

35

Berg
Violin Concerto 26

INTERVAL

Mahler
Symphony No. 10 77
performing version by Deryck Cooke

Thomas Zehetmair *violin*

BBC National Orchestra of Wales
Mark Wigglesworth *conductor*

Deryck Cooke's performing version of Mahler's last symphony was premiered at the 1964 Proms, conducted by Berthold Goldschmidt. In May Mark Wigglesworth – who takes over as Music Director of the BBC National Orchestra of Wales in January – conducted the Tenth during the Royal Concertgebouw Orchestra's Mahler Festival in Amsterdam. The brilliant young Austrian virtuoso plays Berg's poignant final masterpiece, written in memory of Alma Mahler's teenage daughter. For more about Mahler, see Paul Banks on page 22.

Price code A

SATURDAY 19 AUGUST

7.00pm *ending at approximately 9.15pm*

Pre-Prom Talk at 5.45pm
Malcolm Williamson

36 NOTE TIME

Bernstein
Overture 'Candide' 6

Bernstein orch. Sid Ramin
Clarinet Sonata 11
European premiere

Malcolm Williamson
A Year of Birds c35
BBC commission: world premiere

INTERVAL

Copland
Clarinet Concerto 17

Bernstein
Symphonic Dances from
'West Side Story' 22

Richard Stoltzman *clarinet*
Alison Hagley *soprano*

BBC Concert Orchestra
Barry Wordsworth *conductor*

One of the world's most versatile clarinettists, equally at home with jazz, classical and film music, Richard Stoltzman was featured in the television series *Concerto!* playing the Copland Concerto and the Bernstein Sonata, specially orchestrated for him by Sid Ramin, one of the American composer's long-time collaborators. These frame a BBC commission from the Master of the Queen's Music, and the Prom begins and ends with orchestral excerpts from two of Bernstein's Broadway shows.

SPECIAL OFFER!

Price code C

SATURDAY 19 AUGUST

10.15pm *ending at approximately 12.40am*

37

Julian Joseph All-Star Big Band

Part I	60
INTERVAL	
Part 2	60

A late-evening concert of pure enjoyment from the brilliant young British jazz pianist/composer and his All-Star Big Band. After cutting his artistic teeth working with musicians such as Courtney Pine and Steve Williamson, Julian Joseph won a scholarship to study in Boston in 1985, and has since worked with Wynton Marsalis, Bobby McFerrin and Joe Williams. Since 1990 he has toured widely with his own quartet, and released two albums. He has also recently appeared on the BBC television series *Soundbites*, playing the Gershwin Piano Concerto and a piece of his own. His All-Star Big Band includes many famous names, such as Peter King, Steve Williamson and Andy Sheppard on saxes, Guy Barker on trumpet and Tony Remy on guitar.

Price code A

SUNDAY 20 AUGUST

7.30pm *ending at approximately 9.40pm*

38

Beethoven
Overture 'Prometheus' — 5

Sir Michael Tippett
Symphony No. 2 — 34

INTERVAL

Mahler
Symphony No. 4 in G major — 58

Christiane Oelze *soprano*

BBC Symphony Orchestra
Andrew Davis *conductor*

Sir Michael Tippett celebrates his ninetieth birthday this year. As a tribute to Britain's most celebrated living composer the BBC Symphony Orchestra and Andrew Davis perform his Second Symphony, which the orchestra premiered under Sir Adrian Boult in 1958. The inspiration for the symphony came from 'some pounding cello and bass Cs' in a work by Vivaldi which, Tippett says, 'suddenly threw me from Vivaldi's world into my own'. C is also the keynote of Beethoven's most optimistic overture, from his 1801 ballet *The Creatures of Prometheus*.

Price code A

MONDAY 21 AUGUST

7.30pm *ending at approximately 9.45pm*

Pre-Prom Talk at 6.15pm
Poul Ruders

39

Strauss
Till Eulenspiegel — 15

Poul Ruders
Concerto for Viola and Orchestra — 28
UK premiere

INTERVAL

Hindemith
Trauermusik — 9

Nielsen
Symphony No. 4 'Inextinguishable' — 34

Yuri Bashmet *viola*

Danish Radio Symphony Orchestra
Ulf Schirmer *conductor*

Under its new Principal Conductor, the Danish orchestra features two works from its homeland – the British premiere of a concerto played by Yuri Bashmet, and Nielsen's Fourth, a passionate affirmation of the unquenchable power of the human spirit. Despite the sticky end of its madcap hero, Strauss's *Till Eulenspiegel* is one of the most exuberant works in the orchestral repertoire. Hindemith's *Mourning Music*, commissioned by the BBC to commemorate the death of King George V in 1936, was written and performed within the space of two days, and proved to be a masterpiece.

Price code A

TUESDAY 22 AUGUST

7.30pm *ending at approximately 9.35pm*

40

Dvořák
The Water Goblin   22
Lutoslawski
Piano Concerto   27
INTERVAL
Beethoven
Symphony No. 4 in B flat major   34

Ursula Oppens *piano*

The London Philharmonic
Franz Welser-Möst *conductor*

The first two works in tonight's programme
both had their British premieres at the Proms:
Dvořák's tone-poem in 1896 and
Lutoslawski's concerto during the 1989 season. *The Water Goblin* is one of a group of
four tone-poems based on Czech folk-tales
which Dvořák wrote towards the end of his
life. This one concerns a girl who is abducted
by a water goblin, to whom she bears a child.
But when she is allowed to visit her mother
and fails to return, the vindictive goblin
deposits their baby on the doorstep – minus
its head. Ursula Oppens, one of the world's
finest interpreters of contemporary piano
music, has championed Lutoslawski's concerto, which she recently performed with the
Chicago Symphony.

Price code C

WEDNESDAY 23 AUGUST

6.00pm *ending at approximately 7.15pm*

41   NOTE TIME

Naji Hakim
Variations on Two Themes   8
UK premiere
Langlais
Trio from 'Mosaïque'   5
Naji Hakim
Le Tombeau d'Olivier Messiaen   20
UK premiere
Messiaen
La Résurrection du Christ,   7
from 'Livre du Saint Sacrement'
Naji Hakim
Vexilla Regis Prodeunt   10
UK premiere
Improvisation   c12

Naji Hakim *organ*

The Lebanese organist Naji Hakim went to
Paris at the age of twenty to study with Jean
Langlais, sweeping the board of prizes at the
Paris Conservatoire and in every major inter-
national organ competition. From 1985 to
1993 he was organist at the Sacré-Coeur in
Montmartre, and then succeeded Olivier
Messiaen to the important post of organist at
La Trinité. He is now in demand all over the
world as a recitalist, teacher and improviser.

Price code A

WEDNESDAY 23 AUGUST

8.00pm *ending at approximately 10.00pm*

42   NOTE TIME

Schumann
Konzertstück for Four Horns   18
INTERVAL
Mahler
Das klagende Lied   71

Timothy Brown *horn*
Michael Murray *horn*
Andrew Antcliff *horn*
Christopher Larkin *horn*

Lynda Russell *soprano*
Catherine Wyn-Rogers *mezzo-soprano*
Thomas Randle *tenor*
Alan Opie *baritone*

London Philharmonic Choir
BBC Symphony Chorus
BBC Symphony Orchestra
Alexander Lazarev *conductor*

This programme is a gift for horn players.
Mahler's early cantata is imbued with the forest scenes, hunting-calls and wind sonorities
beloved of German composers from Weber to
Wagner, both of whom strongly influenced
Mahler's style. The indefatigable Henry Wood
gave the British premiere of Schumann's marvellous Concert Piece, one of the composer's
most satisfying orchestral works.

Price code B

THURSDAY 24 AUGUST

7.30pm *ending at approximately 9.30pm*

Pre-Prom Talk at 6.15pm
Bernard Rands

Bach orch. Stokowski
Toccata and Fugue in D minor   8

Bernard Rands
Canzone per Orchestra   25
UK premiere

INTERVAL

Brahms
Symphony No. 2 in D major   42

The Philadelphia Orchestra
Wolfgang Sawallisch *conductor*

On the Last Night of the 1994 season the BBC Symphony Orchestra played Henry Wood's orchestration of Bach's famous Toccata and Fugue. Leopold Stokowski's version was written with the sound of the world-famous Philadelphia Orchestra in mind; and they have chosen it to open the first of their two Proms this season. Wolfgang Sawallisch, the Philadelphia's Music Director since 1992, is one of the world's finest Brahms exponents: his many international honours include the Brahms Medal of Hamburg. Bernard Rands, now the Philadelphia's Composer-in-Residence, was born in Sheffield sixty years ago; a former student of Luciano Berio, his music frequently maintains a connection with Italy.

Price code B

FRIDAY 25 AUGUST

7.30pm *ending at approximately 9.40pm*

Schumann
Overture 'Manfred'   12

Hindemith
Cello Concerto   27

INTERVAL

Strauss
Ein Heldenleben   46

Heinrich Schiff *cello*

The Philadelphia Orchestra
Wolfgang Sawallisch *conductor*

Hindemith's concerto was written for performance in America. First played in Boston in 1941 by Gregor Piatigorsky and the Boston Symphony, it is interpreted here by an Austrian virtuoso who has thankfully not entirely forsaken the cello for his parallel career as a conductor. The Philadelphia's conductor, himself born in Munich, spent two decades as Music Director and then Intendant of the Bavarian State Opera, a post occupied by Richard Strauss at the time of the composition of *A Hero's Life*.

Price code A

SATURDAY 26 AUGUST

7.30pm *ending at approximately 9.50pm*

Pre-Prom Talk at 6.15pm
Thea Musgrave

Sibelius
Finlandia   8

Beethoven
Triple Concerto   36

INTERVAL

Thea Musgrave
Excerpts from Act 2 of
'Simón Bolívar'*   28
UK premiere

Sibelius
Symphony No. 5 in E flat major   31

Stephanie Gonley *violin*
Clemens Hagen *cello*
Kathryn Stott *piano*

Amy Johnson *soprano*
Stephen Guggenheim *tenor*
Douglas Nagel *baritone*

BBC Scottish Symphony Orchestra
Osmo Vänskä *conductor*
Peter Mark *conductor**

A trio of young soloists joins the BBC Scottish Symphony Orchestra and the Music Director of the Icelandic Symphony Orchestra for a performance of Beethoven's majestic concerto. Adrian Jack introduces the excerpts from Musgrave's latest opera on page 88.

SUNDAY 27 AUGUST

11.30am *ending at approximately 1.30pm*

46

Young Person's Concert

Bartók
Romanian Folk Dances 6

Ibert
Divertissement 16

Martinů
Le Jazz 4

Gershwin
Rhapsody in Blue 15

INTERVAL

Falla
Ritual Fire Dance from
'Love, the Magician' 4

Satie
Parade 14

Shostakovich
Suite of Dances 16

Jack Gibbons *piano*
New London Orchestra
Ronald Corp *conductor*

This programme, presented by the orchestra's founder/conductor, is designed to appeal to young people aged from around ten upwards. Tickets are half-price for under-14s.

Proms Picnic! *Do join us with your hampers and cool boxes for an informal picnic afterwards in Hyde Park (between Queens Gate and the Albert Memorial). In case of rain: alternative arrangements will be announced on the day.*

Price code A

SUNDAY 27 AUGUST

8.00pm *ending at approximately 9.35pm*

47

Mahler
Symphony No. 9 85

Royal Liverpool Philharmonic Orchestra
Libor Pešek *conductor*

The season's Mahler exploration continues. Under its Principal Conductor and Artistic Adviser Libor Pešek, the Royal Liverpool Philharmonic Orchestra has toured the USA, Germany and Austria, and in 1993 it was invited to open the Prague Spring Festival – the first non-Czech orchestra to be so honoured for many years. The orchestra has also expanded its list of recordings to include Mahler's Ninth with Pešek, and his First and Fifth with Sir Charles Mackerras.

Price code B

MONDAY 28 AUGUST

7.30pm *ending at approximately 9.45pm*

48

Janáček
The Makropulos Case *semi-staged*

Acts 1 & 2 66

INTERVAL

Act 3 30

Glyndebourne Festival Opera

Emilia Marty	Anja Silja *soprano*
Albert Gregor	Kim Begley *tenor*
Vítek	Anthony Roden *tenor*
Kristina	Manuela Kriscak *soprano*
Jaroslav Prus	Victor Braun *baritone*
Janek	Christopher Ventris *tenor*
Dr Kolenatý	Andrew Shore *baritone*
Hauk-Šendorf	Robert Tear *tenor*
A stage dresser	Menai Davies *mezzo-soprano*
Chambermaid	Susan Gorton *soprano*

The Glyndebourne Chorus
The London Philharmonic
Andrew Davis *conductor*

The annual Proms visit of Glyndebourne Festival Opera is always eagerly awaited. This year they follow up the outstanding success of *Katya Kabanova* in 1990 with the spine-chilling story of a woman who appears to have discovered the secret of immortality. The great German soprano Anja Silja sings the role of the enigmatic Emilia Marty. Mark Audus introduces Janáček's opera on page 28.

TUESDAY 29 AUGUST

7.30pm *ending at approximately 9.35pm*

Pre-Prom Talk at 6.15pm
Kaija Saariaho and Esa-Pekka Salonen

Nielsen
Overture 'Helios'   10

Kaija Saariaho
Graal Théâtre   24
BBC commission: world premiere

INTERVAL

Szymanowski
Stabat Mater   24

Skryabin
The Poem of Ecstasy   24

Gidon Kremer *violin*

Judith Howarth *soprano*
Randi Stene *mezzo-soprano*
Jason Howard *baritone*

BBC Symphony Chorus
BBC Symphony Orchestra
Esa-Pekka Salonen *conductor*

The Music Director of the Los Angeles Philharmonic directs a programme of highly colouristic twentieth-century works. Gidon Kremer – a champion of the works of living composers, and founder of a chamber-music festival focusing on new music – is the soloist in a work commissioned jointly by the BBC and the Helsinki Festival. Szymanowski's hieratic masterpiece, which has recently gained wide popular acceptance, forms a striking contrast to the unashamedly erotic nature of Skryabin's *Poem of Ecstasy*.

WEDNESDAY 30 AUGUST

7.30pm *ending at approximately 9.40pm*

Richard Meale
Very High Kings   13
UK premiere

Canteloube
Songs of the Auvergne: 20
  1 Baïlèro
  2 Lo Fiolaire
  3 La Delaïssádo
  4 Trois Bourrées

INTERVAL

Strauss
An Alpine Symphony   50

Yvonne Kenny *soprano*

Sydney Symphony Orchestra
Edo de Waart *conductor*

Australian soprano Yvonne Kenny joins the Sydney orchestra on a welcome return visit to the Proms for Canteloube's ravishing arrangements of songs from the mountainous Auvergne region of central France. Even higher peaks are explored in Strauss's sumptuous tone-poem, describing a day in the mountains that the composer could see from his study window in Garmisch. Richard Meale is one of Australia's senior composers, and the influence of things Spanish – in this instance 'the mystical voyage of Christopher Columbus' – runs throughout his work.

THURSDAY 31 AUGUST

7.00pm *ending at approximately 9.10pm*

Pre-Prom Talk at 5.45pm
Edo de Waart
and Mary Vallentine

Berlioz
Overture 'Beatrice and Benedict'   8

Schoenberg
Pelleas and Melisande   42

INTERVAL

Beethoven
Violin Concerto in D major   44

Vadim Repin *violin*

Sydney Symphony Orchestra
Edo de Waart *conductor*

Tonight's soloist, winner of the Wieniawski International Competition at the age of eleven and of the Queen Elisabeth of the Belgians Competition at seventeen, and still only in his early twenties, is being hailed as one of the finest young Russian violinists to emerge since David Oistrakh. Here he joins the Sydney Symphony and its Music Director in the Beethoven concerto, one of the most difficult from the interpretative point of view. Schoenberg's symphonic poem inspired by Maeterlinck's symbolist drama was written around the time of the first production of Debussy's opera on the subject, though its evocation of the twilit kingdom of Allemonde is very different.

Price code C

THURSDAY 31 AUGUST

10.00pm *ending at approximately 11.00pm*

Shostakovich
Symphony No. 14   55

Nancy Gustafson *soprano*
John Tomlinson *bass*

The Premiere Ensemble
Mark Wigglesworth *conductor*

Mark Wigglesworth and his acclaimed ensemble combine forces with two international stars for a performance of Shostakovich's penultimate symphony. It consists of settings for two solo voices, strings and percussion of sombre texts by a variety of nineteenth- and twentieth-century poets. Rilke's *Conclusion* sums up the mood of the whole work: 'Death is all-powerful, keeping watch even in the hour of the highest happiness, living and longing and mourning in us'.

Price code A

FRIDAY 1 SEPTEMBER

7.30pm *ending at approximately 9.35pm*

Weber
Overture 'Der Freischütz'   10
Brahms
Piano Concerto No. 2 in B flat major   49
INTERVAL
Hindemith
Sancta Susanna   25

Susanna	Susan Bullock *soprano*
Klementia	Eva Randová *mezzo-soprano*
Old Nun	Ann Howard *mezzo-soprano*

The Sixteen *women's voices*

Garrick Ohlsson *piano*

BBC Philharmonic
Yan Pascal Tortelier *conductor*

Last January, as part of the BBC's Hindemith Festival, London audiences had a chance to hear the first UK performance of his one-act drama *Sancta Susanna*, a dark and horrifying study of sexual hysteria in a nunnery. Its first performance in 1922 aroused howls of protest and led to its inevitable withdrawal during the Nazi régime. Now there's a second chance to hear the same cast in this explosive mixture of sex and religion.

Price code A

SATURDAY 2 SEPTEMBER

7.30pm *ending at approximately 9.45pm*

Mozart
Piano Concerto No. 14
in E flat major, K449   22
INTERVAL
Mahler
Symphony No. 7   80

Leon McCawley *piano*
Bournemouth Symphony Orchestra
Andrew Litton *conductor*

Andrew Litton, who this year hands over the Chief Conductorship of tonight's orchestra after a highly successful tenure, joins this season's pantheon of Mahler conductors. Leon McCawley, runner-up in the final of the 1993 Leeds International Piano Competition, and a young pianist of supreme sensitivity, plays a work by Mozart written for his Viennese pupil Barbara Ployer during his *annus mirabilis* of concerto writing in 1784.

Price code A

SUNDAY 3 SEPTEMBER

7.30pm *ending at approximately 9.05pm*

Britten
War Requiem 85

Christine Brewer *soprano*
John Mark Ainsley *tenor*
Andreas Schmidt *baritone*

Bach Choir
London Choral Society
Choristers of St Paul's Cathedral
Nash Ensemble
Royal Philharmonic Orchestra
Jane Glover *conductor*

This year Europe commemorates the ending of World War II fifty years ago. Tonight's concert, scheduled on the anniversary of its outbreak, comprises one of the greatest musical works born of that devastating conflict. First performed to mark the consecration of Coventry's new cathedral in May 1962, Britten's intensely moving piece meditates on the pity and horror of war in a spirit of reconciliation. The German baritone Andreas Schmidt is joined by the British tenor John Mark Ainsley and American soprano Christine Brewer, while Jane Glover directs the RPO. The chamber orchestra part is taken by the Nash Ensemble, currently celebrating a triumphant thirtieth-birthday season.

NB There will be no interval in this performance.

Price code A

MONDAY 4 SEPTEMBER

7.30pm *ending at approximately 9.40pm*

Pre-Prom Talk at 6.15pm
Jonathan Harvey

Debussy
Prélude à l'après-midi d'un faune 8
Peter Eötvös
Psychokosmos 16
UK premiere
Bartók
Piano Concerto No. 2 29
INTERVAL
Jonathan Harvey
Madonna of Winter and Spring 36

Márta Fábián *cimbalom*
Peter Frankl *piano*
BBC Symphony Orchestra
Peter Eötvös *conductor*

The Principal Guest Conductor of the BBC Symphony Orchestra from 1985 to 1988 returns to direct a repeat performance of Harvey's work for orchestra, synthesizers and electronics enthusiastically received at its Prom premiere in 1986. Since 1985 Eötvös has been professor at the International Bartók Seminar at Szombathely in Hungary, and the example of Bartók has been crucial to his own development as a composer. A work of his for solo cimbalom and orchestra receives its British premiere tonight, framed by two twentieth-century classics.

SPECIAL OFFER!

Price code B

TUESDAY 5 SEPTEMBER

7.30pm *ending at approximately 9.40pm*

Berg orch. Theo Verbey
Piano Sonata 14
UK premiere
Mahler
Lieder eines fahrenden Gesellen 18
INTERVAL
Mahler
Symphony No. 1 in D major 54

Wolfgang Holzmair *baritone*
Royal Concertgebouw Orchestra
Riccardo Chailly *conductor*

Mahler dominates this programme given by the Royal Concertgebouw Orchestra under its Principal Conductor. During his tenure, Chailly has concentrated on the orchestra's strengths in the Austro-German symphonic repertoire while also focusing on the twentieth century. An Austrian baritone acclaimed for intelligent interpretations and refined quality of tone makes his debut in Mahler's achingly poignant song-cycle, whose folk-inspired melodies in turn imbue the fabric of the First Symphony. The programme opens with a contemporary Dutch musician's orchestration of an early piece by a composer greatly influenced by Mahler.

WEDNESDAY 6 SEPTEMBER

Price code B

7.00pm *ending at approximately 9.15pm*

Pre-Prom Talk at 5.45pm
Riccardo Chailly

Debussy
La Mer 24

Messiaen
Oiseaux Exotiques 14

INTERVAL

Ravel
Piano Concerto in G major 22

Stravinsky
The Firebird – suite (1945) 29

Jean-Yves Thibaudet *piano*
Royal Concertgebouw Orchestra
Riccardo Chailly *conductor*

From Austria to France for the Concertgebouw's second Prom. The French pianist, a favourite guest artist with the orchestra (with which he has made an award-winning recording of Messiaen's *Turangalîla Symphony*), returns after his sensational performance last season of Ravel's dark-hued Concerto for Left Hand, for the glittering G major Concerto, a combination of brilliance and tender sensuality, and for one of Messiaen's tributes to birds – 'the greatest musicians to inhabit our planet'. Two other masterpieces shot through with ravishing orchestral effects complete an unmissable programme.

WEDNESDAY 6 SEPTEMBER

Price code D

10.00pm *ending at approximately 11.30pm*

Purcell
Dido and Aeneas *semi-staged* 70

Opera Atelier

Dido	Linda Maguire *mezzo-soprano*
Aeneas	Brett Polegato *baritone*
Belinda	Shari Saunders *soprano*
Sorceress	Jacques François Loiseleur de Longchamps *baritone*

with
Benjamin Butterfield *tenor*
Laura Pudwell *mezzo-soprano*
Meredith Hall *soprano*

Polyphony
Les Musiciens du Louvre
Marc Minkowski *conductor*

No celebration of Purcell's tercentenary would be complete without a performance of his best-known work. This production, staged in Toronto and Houston last winter, draws on contemporary accounts of Baroque staging and features lavish costumes and spectacular choreography. Under Marc Minkowski, a leading Baroque ensemble makes its debut in this legendary tale of passion and betrayal, exploring previously unplumbed depths of emotional intensity.

THURSDAY 7 SEPTEMBER

Price code A

7.00pm *ending at approximately 9.30pm*

Pre-Prom Talk at 5.45pm
Steve Reich

Antheil
Ballet Mécanique 22

INTERVAL

Steve Reich
City Life 25

Proverbs 15
BBC commission: world premiere

INTERVAL

Stravinsky
Les Noces 23

Melanie Armitstead *soprano*
Fiona Kimm *mezzo-soprano*
Gunnar Gudbjörnsson *tenor*
Mikhail Krutikov *baritone*

BBC Singers
Ensemble Modern
Peter Eötvös *conductor*

A fascinating programme from the highly acclaimed twentieth-century ensemble featuring the dynamic combination of pianos and percussion. Both Antheil's extraordinary *Ballet mécanique*, created in Paris in 1924 to accompany an abstract film by Fernand Léger, and Stravinsky's ritualised ballet score, first performed in Paris in 1923, require the services of four pianists plus percussion. Adrian Jack introduces the Reich pieces on page 88.

SPECIAL OFFER!

FRIDAY 8 SEPTEMBER

7.30pm *ending at approximately 9.40pm*

Pre-Prom Talk at 6.15pm
Nicholas Maw

Nicholas Maw
The World in the Evening   29

INTERVAL

Beethoven
Symphony No. 9 in D minor 'Choral'   70

Janice Watson *soprano*
Della Jones *mezzo-soprano*
Paul Charles Clarke *tenor*
Gwynne Howell *bass*

BBC Welsh Chorus
BBC Symphony Chorus
BBC National Orchestra of Wales
Tadaaki Otaka *conductor*

The traditional Prom performance of Beethoven's Ninth Symphony this season falls to the BBC National Orchestra of Wales under Tadaaki Otaka in his last Prom as the orchestra's Chief Conductor. Nicholas Maw, who first shot to fame with his ecstatically lyrical 1962 Proms commission *Scenes and Arias*, celelebrates his sixtieth birthday this year. *The World in the Evening* was written for the Orchestra of the Royal Opera House, Covent Garden, in 1988. Maw describes it as 'evoking a general feeling of evening in several different senses: a time of day, a time of life, a state of mind, and a state of the world'.

SATURDAY 9 SEPTEMBER

7.30pm *ending at approximately 9.20pm*

Mozart
Symphony No. 40 in G minor   27

INTERVAL

Tchaikovsky
Symphony No. 5 in E minor   48

BBC Symphony Orchestra
Günter Wand *conductor*

One of the world's most distinguished conductors directs this programme of popular classics. Much beloved of all string and wind players, Mozart's concise but deeply expressive penultimate symphony is paired with Tchaikovsky's Fifth, a smash-hit with audiences ever since its first performance in 1888, underpinned (like the Mozart) with private 'murmurs, doubts and complaints' at the unpredictable designs of Providence.

SUNDAY 10 SEPTEMBER

7.30pm *ending at approximately 9.45pm*

Nielsen
Symphony No. 3 'Sinfonia espansiva'   38

INTERVAL

Elgar
Cello Concerto in E minor   29

Prokofiev
Romeo and Juliet – Suite No. 2   27

Susan Chilcott *soprano*
David Mattinson *baritone*

Natalia Gutman *cello*

Royal Scottish National Orchestra
Neeme Järvi *conductor*

Under its Conductor Laureate, the Royal Scottish National Orchestra begins its 1995 Prom with Nielsen's *Sinfonia espansiva*, written in 1911. As its title suggests, this work is a hymn to life, conveying a deep love of his native Danish countryside. In a magical passage in the second movement, the orchestra is augmented by two wordless solo voices. The brilliant Russian cellist Natalia Gutman salutes the memory of Jacqueline du Pré (who would have celebrated her fiftieth birthday this year) in Elgar's poignant masterpiece.

MONDAY 11 SEPTEMBER

7.30pm *ending at approximately 10.00pm*

Pre-Prom Talk at 6.15pm
James Wood

Busnois
In hydraulis 9

Machaut
Messe de Notre Dame 25

Iannis Xenakis
Okho 15

Trad.
Timbila Music from Mozambique 20

INTERVAL

James Wood
Two men meet, each presuming
the other to be from a distant planet 18
BBC commission: world premiere

Messiaen
Couleurs de la Cité Céleste 16

The Hilliard Ensemble

The Hague Percussion Group
Venancio Mbande *timbila*

Steven Schick *percussion*

Andrew Ball *piano*

Critical Band
James Wood *conductor*

Musicians from Africa, America and Europe combine in a programme driven by rhythm. Venancio Mbande is one of the finest exponents of the timbila – a kind of xylophone played by the Chopi people of Southern Mozambique, usually in orchestras of between ten and twenty instruments. The American virtuoso Steven Schick gives the world premiere of a percussion concerto by one of Britain's most imaginative musicians, who talks to Adrian Jack elsewhere in the Guide. Rhythmic subtlety adds to the fascination of two early French vocal pieces: that by Antoine Busnois, dating from the mid-fifteenth century, sets a text by Pythagoras – one of the earliest of all musical theorists – while the Machaut mass, probably written for Rheims Cathedral, shows what mastery of rhythmic patterns had been attained one hundred years earlier. The exotic rhythms of Greece and India motivate the striking colours of Messiaen's vision of the heavenly city, while Xenakis's work for percussion features a large African drum.

SPECIAL OFFER!

TUESDAY 12 SEPTEMBER

7.30pm *ending at approximately 9.40pm*

Rakhmaninov
The Isle of the Dead 20

Bernd Alois Zimmermann
Photoptosis 13

Liszt
Totentanz 15

INTERVAL

Musorgsky orch. Ravel
Pictures at an Exhibition 33

Rolf Hind *piano*

Junge Deutsche Philharmonie
Markus Stenz *conductor*

Music and pictures are the subject of this interesting programme from Germany's national youth orchestra, making its Prom debut. Markus Stenz, a former Tanglewood protégé of Ozawa and Bernstein, is rising to fame throughout Europe both in opera (he has conducted many of Henze's latest works, and recently made his ENO debut with a new production of *Don Giovanni*) and in concert. The brilliant young British pianist Rolf Hind, rapidly making a name as an outstanding interpreter of the contemporary repertoire, plays Liszt's fearsome *Totentanz*. Andrew Huth discusses the relationship between the aural and visual arts on page 40.

WEDNESDAY 13 SEPTEMBER

7.00pm *ending at approximately 9.10pm*

Pre-Prom Talk at 5.45pm
Elliott Carter

Elliott Carter
Adagio tenebroso 20
BBC commission: world premiere

Elgar
Falstaff 34

INTERVAL

Brahms
Violin Concerto in D major 40

Frank Peter Zimmermann *violin*

BBC Symphony Orchestra
Andrew Davis *conductor*

Elliott Carter's new work forms the central panel of a large-scale orchestral triptych written for three different orchestras (Part I for the Chicago Symphony and Part III for the New York Philharmonic). Renowned for his Elgar interpretations, Andrew Davis conducts one of the composer's finest works, a sympathetic and touching portrait of Shakespeare's uninhibited and rumbustious knight – a character far removed from Elgar's decorous Edwardian world.

WEDNESDAY 13 SEPTEMBER

10.00pm *ending at approximately 11.25pm*

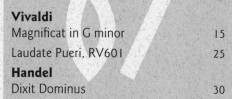

Vivaldi
Magnificat in G minor 15
Laudate Pueri, RV601 25

Handel
Dixit Dominus 30

Lillian Watson *soprano*

Gabrieli Consort and Players
Paul McCreesh *conductor*

With their founder/conductor, the Gabrieli Consort and Players have built up an international reputation for period-instrument performances and spectacular reconstructions of actual historical musical events. Their highly-praised *A Venetian Coronation 1595*, heard at the Proms in 1992, won a *Gramophone* award. Their Prom this season offers vocal works from Vivaldi's Venice and Handel's period in Rome, with Lillian Watson taking the florid solo part in the virtuoso cantata *Laudate Pueri*.

THURSDAY 14 SEPTEMBER

7.30pm *ending at approximately 9.55pm*

Bartók
Duke Bluebeard's Castle 58

Judith   Markella Hatziano *mezzo-soprano*
Duke Bluebeard   Robert Hale *baritone*

INTERVAL

Ravel
L'Enfant et les sortilèges 50

The Child   Catherine Dubosc *soprano*
with
Hélène Perraguin *mezzo-soprano*
Delphine Haidan *mezzo-soprano*
Elisabeth Vidal *soprano*
Jeannette Fischer *soprano*
Michel Sénéchal *tenor*
François Le Roux *baritone*
René Schirrer *bass*

New London Children's Choir
London Symphony Chorus
London Symphony Orchestra
Kent Nagano *conductor*

Kent Nagano, Associate Principal Guest Conductor of the London Symphony Orchestra, is also musical director of the Opéra de Lyon. For this programme he brings a star team of French singers to join the LSO in a concert performance of Ravel's bewitching one-act opera about childhood, based on a libretto by Colette. Bartók receives a final tribute with his brooding, mysterious opera on the Bluebeard legend, premiered in Budapest in 1918.

Price code A

FRIDAY 15 SEPTEMBER

7.30pm *ending at approximately 9.20pm*

Pre-Prom Talk at 6.15pm
Luciano Berio

Luciano Berio
New work   8
BBC commission: world premiere

Mahler
Symphony No. 2 in C minor
'Resurrection'   85

BBC Singers
Simon Joly *conductor*

Rosa Mannion *soprano*
Jean Rigby *mezzo-soprano*

Brighton Festival Chorus
Edinburgh Festival Chorus
BBC Philharmonic
Sir Charles Mackerras *conductor*

Few conductors can command respect over such a wide and varied repertoire as Sir Charles Mackerras: his expertise ranges from Handel and Mozart to twentieth-century British and Czech music. Luciano Berio has always acknowledged the influence of Mahler: one movement of his *Sinfonia* is modelled on the scherzo of Mahler's Second Symphony. His new unaccompanied choral piece has been written specially for the BBC Singers, whom Berio has described as 'a jewel in the crown of English performance'.

NB There will be no interval in this performance.

Price code E

SATURDAY 16 SEPTEMBER

7.30pm *ending at approximately 10.40pm*

Berlioz
Overture 'The Corsair'   8
Vaughan Williams
The Lark Ascending   14
Zemlinsky
Psalm 23   11
Mahler
Songs from
'Des Knaben Wunderhorn'   12
Strauss
Waltz Sequence No. 1 from
'Der Rosenkavalier'   11

INTERVAL

Sir Harrison Birtwistle
Panic   15
BBC commission: world premiere
Boccherini arr. Berio
Ritirata notturna di Madrid   7
Purcell arr. Stokowski
Dido's Lament from
'Dido and Aeneas'   5

Saint-Saëns
Introduction and Rondo Capriccioso   9
Elgar
Pomp and Circumstance March No. 1   6
Henry Wood
Fantasia on British Sea-Songs   12
Arne
Rule, Britannia!   5
Parry orch. Elgar
Jerusalem   2

Tasmin Little *violin*
Catherine Wyn-Rogers *mezzo-soprano*

John Harle *saxophone*
Paul Clarvis *drummer*

BBC Singers
BBC Symphony Chorus
BBC Symphony Orchestra
Andrew Davis *conductor*

Apart from an engaging trifle by Boccherini (wittily arranged by Luciano Berio) representing the tattoo recalling soldiers to their barracks in eighteenth-century Madrid, this year's Last Night is notable for a substantial commission from Sir Harrison Birtwistle specially written for tonight's saxophonist and drummer, and described among Adrian Jack's Centenary Novelties on page 88.

Commentary by Wendy Thompson

GARDNER MERCHANT
RING & BRYMER
FOOD AND DRINK
AT
THE ROYAL ALBERT HALL

ELGAR ROOM RESTAURANT and VICTORIA RESTAURANT

On the Balcony Level (enter by Door 8 and Door 5)
These beautifully decorated rooms offer a full Waiter Service
Restaurant with a Selection of Dishes every day

Open Daily from 5.30pm

Table Reservations Possible

PRINCE CONSORT ROOM

wine bar is situated on the
Grand Tier (enter via Doors 13/14)
serving a Selection of Freshly Made Sandwiches,
Pastries plus a daily Hot Dish with Vegetarian Alternatives

Full Bar Facilities

Open Daily from 5.30pm

PRIVATE BOXES AND BANQUETING ROOMS

Catering with personal service is available in all private boxes and banqueting rooms
(to be consumed before the concert and during the interval only)

For advice and/or information about the range and variety of food and drink which may be ordered in advance please telephone
The Ring & Brymer Catering Office

(orders must be placed at least 48 hours before the Show)

BARS

Bars are available on all Levels
offering a wide selection of Alcoholic Drinks, Beverages
& Sandwiches

INTERVAL – ORDERS

All of our Bars and The Prince Consort Room situated
on all levels of the Hall offer the facility to
pre-order your interval drinks

Only Food and Drink purchased within the Royal Albert Hall may be consumed on the premises

For all Restaurant Bookings and Catering Enquiries
Telephone 0171-589 8900

RING & BRYMER
Caterers of Distinction since 1690

CENTENARY NOVELTIES

Adrian Jack previews some of the wealth of music new to the Proms this year

THE PROMS usually take present-day music in their stride. In this centenary year, the particular emphasis on commissioned pieces balances the retrospective character of the hundredth season in 1994. There are no fewer than fourteen commissions, plus a substantial number of recent works being introduced to this country.

For the Last Night Sir Harrison Birtwistle promises a 'dithyramb' for John Harle's alto saxophone with drum kit and orchestra. This is a bold choice, because Birtwistle is not a lightweight composer and he is not likely to modify his bold, rugged style for the sake of easy appeal. The *Oxford English Dictionary* defines 'dithyramb' as a 'Greek choric hymn ... wild and vehement in character'. The piece's title *Panic* derives from an ancient Greek source as well: the Greek god Pan loved music and invented the syrinx, or shepherd's flute. He was dreaded by travellers, to whom he would suddenly appear and inspire them with fear (or 'panic'). Ancient Greek myths and literature have been a constant thread in Birtwistle's music for many years – one of his operas is based on the legend of Orpheus. He usually works on a grand, expansive time-scale, so for him, at roughly fifteen minutes, *Panic* is relatively short, though his recent *The Cry of Anubis*, a concerto for tuba and orchestra, was also about that length.

The youngest composer to be commissioned for the Proms this year is Benedict Mason, who's something of a maverick, his music often referring to a complex background of other composers' pieces. Last year Mason hit the headlines with *Playing Away*, an opera about football (though, oddly enough, Mason is not actually a fan) to a libretto by Howard Brenton (who *is* a fan). Mason's last BBC commission was a Concerto for the Viola Section – not just

Far left: 'Pan and his pipes' by Paulus Moreelse (1571–1638)

Sir Harrison Birtwistle

a solo viola – which turned an old joke about the retiring nature of viola-players into a serious and highly complex piece of music. (Mason himself was once a viola player in the National Youth Orchestra.)

Mason's success has been remarkably rapid, based on pieces he's written in the last ten years. But still more recent is the interest which two much younger composers, Thomas Adès and Julian Anderson, have attracted; they are both in their mid-twenties. Adès is Composer-in-Residence with the Hallé Orchestra, and they bring his music in their programme in Prom 14, sandwiched between Webern and Mahler. Adès graduated from Cambridge University in 1992, and won the Cambridge University Musical Society composition prize. As a result he was commissioned to write ... *but all shall be well* for the CUMS Orchestra, which gave its first performance last year. The London Sinfonietta plays Anderson's *Khorovod* (a 'round' or 'circle' dance – Stravinsky used the title in *The Rite of Spring*, and there's a distinct Russian flavour to Anderson's piece), which they commissioned and premiered last winter; they perform it in the same concert as Mason's Clarinet Concerto (Prom 33).

Composers often go abroad to study – Malcolm Williamson originally came from Australia to this country to study with Elisabeth Lutyens and Erwin Stein, and then he stayed here. Lyell Cresswell came from New Zealand to Aberdeen University and, except for two years as Music Organiser at the Chapter Arts Centre in Cardiff, has stayed in Scotland ever since. Composers settle where there is suitable work, often in the form of teaching posts

Benedict Mason

which allow time to write – that's the case with the Yorkshireman Bernard Rands, who has lived in the United States for several years and is now Professor of Composition at Harvard University and Composer-in-Residence with the Philadelphia Orchestra; they play his *Canzone per Orchestra* in Prom 43.

Sir Peter Maxwell Davies was driven by his own demon to the weather-beaten remoteness of Hoy in the Orkney Islands. Davies identifies particularly closely with the remarkably rich culture, not to mention the economic and social concerns, of his adopted home, and Hoy's past and present have provided the explicit subjects of many of his pieces. He describes his commission for the BBC Philharmonic's tour of the USA earlier this year as a 'choreographic poem': it's about the conflict in the seventeenth century between a new Protestant minister on Hoy and his congregation, which was still attached to the ancient pagan ritual of Beltane Fire, celebrating the coming of spring and the renewal of life. Each community lit bonfires, and the celebration continued through the night with dancing and feasting while the young men asserted their masculinity by jumping through the flames.

A great deal of the new music this year seems to be about something, even if it's less picturesque and specific than Davies's piece, or on the most general level of the human predicament. Which is a natural start-

Sir Peter Maxwell Davies

89

John Casken

MALCOLM CROWTHERS

Kaija Saariaho

ing-point for concertos, pitting the individual – or the few – against the many. John Casken, born in Yorkshire and currently Professor at Manchester University, has already written a Cello Concerto for Heinrich Schiff, but his new Violin Concerto (Prom 7) is bigger and is scored for a large orchestra. Casken says 'it's very much a *singing* concerto', written with the Russian violinist Dmitry Sitkovetsky in mind. He describes the first movement as 'passionate and restless – a narrative in which the violinist is a human character responding to musical situations, encountering storms and trials'. He thinks the traditional idea of large symphonic works in several movements is returning, and his concerto roughly follows the standard plan of three movements in the sequence fast–slow–fast. The second movement is private and withdrawn, the last savage and – again, in a traditional mould – recalls ideas from the first two movements in a new light.

The Finnish composer Kaija Saariaho is not a traditional composer in Casken's sense: she does not write lyrical lines, or themes, but concentrates

MALCOLM CROWTHERS

composer whose success has been recent and quite sudden, with commissions and performances springing up everywhere over the last two years. Moving to Scotland (which is not her own country but her husband's) and becoming a mother liberated her creative drive. The viola concerto is not her first – a violin concerto was given its premiere and broadcast in January this year – but it is the first work she has written for her own instrument, though she won't be playing it. She is quite frank about its programmatic basis – Peter's denial of Christ (there is actually a cock crowing) – which is related to her own renewal of Christian faith, and faith in herself as a composer.

The viola is often regarded as the Cinderella of the orchestra, though these days, it's enjoying the limelight as never before. In his Concerto for Viola (Prom 38) the Danish composer Poul Ruders asserts what he calls 'the right and ability of music to stay aloof, maintaining its emotional integrity, detached from the tyranny of fashion and trend'. It seems a vein in which the

Poul Ruders

Above left: *The Round Table and the Holy Grail*

Below:
Attrib. Gabriel Metsu(1629–67) 'The Denial of St Peter'

instead on colour, texture and slow change, which draws her to electronic media. Nevertheless, the playing of the Latvian-born violinist Gidon Kremer encouraged her to write in the traditional concerto form, taking a break from her recent interest in extending the sound of acoustic instruments with electronics. The title of her concerto, *Graal Théâtre*, performed by Kremer in Prom 49, is taken from a book by Jacques Roubaud, and suggests a psychological scenario not unlike Casken's. Saariaho talks of the theatrical aspect of performance and the 'delicate sound' of the violin interacting with the orchestra.

Sally Beamish

The soloist in Sally Beamish's Viola Concerto (Prom 16) represents, to some extent, herself. She was, for a time, principal violist in the London Mozart Players, then in the Scottish Chamber Orchestra; she also played a lot of contemporary music as a freelance musician. Beamish is another

James Wood

Judith Bingham

mellow sound of the instrument might be particularly appropriate, and Ruders says his concerto is 'in reality one melodic line only – one tune constantly regenerating itself. It's a musical tribute to serenity and patience'.

James Wood is a composer who is still highly active as a performer. He's a conductor, and a distinguished percussionist, who started building his own instruments when he was at school. He is also very interested in the music of non-European cultures – Asia, the Far East and Africa, where percussion instruments have been of central importance to music for many centuries. Last year Wood completed a concerto for quarter-tone marimba, which he conducted at the Pompidou Centre in Paris. 'I have always wanted to write a percussion concerto', he says.

Two men meet, each presuming the other to be from a distant planet (Prom 64) takes its title from an early etching by Paul Klee: *Two gentlemen bowing to one another, each supposing the other to be in a higher position.* This suggested to Wood the encounter of two parties who don't understand each other but explore ways in which they can communicate. He says the outcome is not settled. Wood has built a set of thirteen wooden drums himself, modelling them on ones made by the German composer Volker Staub. They provide the rhythmic interest in his piece, though compared with most drums their sound is also rich in pitch content. But the soloist's main source of melodic interest is a set of cowbells, which should carry against the twenty-four-piece ensemble more effectively than most pitched percussion.

Judith Bingham is a member of the BBC Singers and was in the BBC Symphony Chorus before she became a professional. She studied composition with Alan Bush, Eric Fenby and Hans Keller – a piquant combination of influences – and she has developed her twin careers of singer and composer over the last twenty years with remarkable success. Many important commissions include two from the BBC Philharmonic; her second work for them will be performed next year. She calls *Salt in the Blood* (Prom 15) 'a ghost story at sea'. She has compiled the text herself, and cast the women in the role of the weather. 'I've done a bit of sailing', she adds reassuringly, 'and I can tell you, you *become* the weather!' The men sing sea-shanties and Bingham has set some of Beaufort's scale to music.

Luciano Berio

The BBC Singers began their seventieth-anniversary celebrations last autumn, and that's marked by commissions from Luciano Berio, Steve Reich and Judith Weir. The voice has always been important in Berio's music, and his new piece is coupled with Mahler's Second Symphony (Prom 69). Berio took the scherzo of Mahler's symphony as the basis for a movement in *Sinfonia*, given its UK premiere at the Proms in 1969 and performed in last year's season. *Sinfonia* is one of his own most spectacular works, in which voices are inseparable from the orchestral mêlée.

In *Moon and Star* (Prom 27), Judith Weir adopts a similar approach, since the voices are treated as a strand in the orchestral texture. Over the last few years she has been much occupied with the theatre – *Blond Eckbert*, her most recently completed opera, was given its first production by English National Opera last year. But in *Moon and Star* she does not try to communicate a text in the same way: words are of secondary importance to the sound-colours of voices in their own right. The text is fragmentary; it functions, she suggests, 'rather as the captions of abstract paintings can sometimes intensify the essence of the picture'.

The word, indeed the Word of God, delivered by an American Evangelical preacher, was the basis of Steve Reich's discovery of what he calls 'music as a gradual process'. He made tape loops of the recorded phrase 'It's gonna rain', and other snatches of the preacher's address, ran them simultaneously and allowed them gradually to move out of phase. During the next few years he explored, exhaustively, processes which ran themselves and which were essentially about rhythm. Reich's development since 1973 has been increasingly interventionist, or inventive in the traditional sense of composing; he has taken on board both harmony and melody. He has also become interested in religious and cultural

Behind the mask: Judith Weir

Peter Eötvös

Steve Reich

associations, particularly Jewish. In 1976–7 he studied the singing and recitation of Hebrew scriptures, which resulted in *Tehillim*, in which he set verses from the Psalms. This was followed by *The Desert Music* (setting poetry by William Carlos Williams), of which the BBC Singers gave the British premiere at the Proms in 1985 and which they have performed several times since, 'always with distinction', says Reich. His commission for the Singers in this year's season is called *Proverbs*, and like *Tehillim* includes texts from the Bible. Scored for six voices (amplified), two pianos and percussion, it breaks with the method of composing with pre-recorded samples which Reich has recently favoured in *Different Trains*, *The Cave* and *City Life*.

City Life shares the same concert as *Proverbs* (Prom 60) and extends the twentieth-century idea that everyday sounds can be included in music. Reich goes a lot further than Gershwin with his car-horns in *An American in Paris*: samples of car-horns, door-slams, air-brakes, pile-drivers, car alarms, boat horns, buoys and sirens are all part of the fabric of the piece, played live on two sampling keyboards.

Reich's pieces will be conducted by Peter Eötvös, who appears in another programme (Prom 56) as the composer of *Psychokosmos*, which he also conducts. Eötvös is best known in this country, in fact,

as a conductor, particularly of the BBC Symphony Orchestra. He was born and grew up in Budapest, and *Psychokosmos* features the Hungarian national instrument, the cimbalom. Eötvös's ambitious title reflects music of strong drama and a compelling, haunted atmosphere. But he avoids any sense of nostalgia or the characteristic style of cimbalom music, which you can still hear in cafés and restaurants if you go to Hungary. Yet the work does, in a sense, look back. In 1961 he wrote a piano piece called *Kosmos*, a reflection on the endless prospect of outer space, then newly opened up by space travel. Thirty-two years later he has taken a look *inwards*, at the unknown depths of his own being. Eötvös is now fifty-one, and he compares the new work to a painter making, from memory, a portrait of himself as a youth.

Lyell Cresswell

94

Lyell Cresswell's concerto (Prom 22) features an instrument which is even more rarely heard in the concert hall than the cimbalom. You might wonder why, once you have heard the remarkable versatility of the Scottish accordionist, James Crabb, who has created a whole new repertoire for his instrument and has enlarged its personality. Cresswell has already written two concertos, a short one for violin and a full-length one for cello. He says he doesn't think it appropriate to call the new work a concerto, even though it is a full-scale piece with three movements, so he's given it the Icelandic name for the solo instrument, *Dragspil*. 'I've never written for the accordion before and do not play it, but James Crabb has given me a good demonstration. As I complete each section of the solo part I send it to him to make sure it works.' At an early stage, he says, he listened to some recordings

Tan Dun

of works for accordion and orchestra to get some idea of the sound and of the balance problems. Then he stopped, he says, 'to avoid contamination'.

A much rarer sound, of the Chinese 'xun' – an ancient ceramic wind instrument with a remote, whispering sound – evokes the sense of another culture at the start of *Orchestral Theatre I* by the Chinese composer Tan Dun, who now lives in New York. Tan grew up in a remote village in Hunan, and in his late teens, during the Cultural Revolution in the mid-1970s, he was sent to a commune to plant rice for two years. In 1978 he was one of the few students to get a place in the re-opened Central Conservatory in Beijing. After 1980 the Conservatory invited guest lecturers including Alexander Goehr and Hans Werner Henze. Chinese students came to grips with Western music fast. During the next few years Tan established his own reputation as a composer in China, with works

including a symphony and a string quartet which won a prize in Germany. In 1986 he was offered a fellowship at Columbia University in New York. Since then his music has been played by orchestras and ensembles around the world, and is this year featured in festivals in Paris and Oslo.

Tan draws on his early experiences of Chinese village life in *Orchestral Theatre I*: he wrote it for the BBC Scottish Symphony Orchestra (with whom he is Associate Composer/Conductor), who gave the first performance at the Edinburgh Festival in 1990; they bring it to London in Prom 24. Conducted by Tan, the orchestral players have to yell, murmur, chant and sing. In *Orchestral Theatre II*, in the same programme, the audience gets a chance to join in as well.

Tan Dun recently finished an opera about Marco Polo to a libretto by the English music critic and novelist Paul Griffiths. The subject of travel and exploration is a potent source of inspiration for composers, who often feel as if they are discovering or searching for new territory themselves. Richard Meale's name rarely appears on concert programmes in the UK, yet he is one of Australia's most distinguished composers. Like many Australian composers, he's been drawn to the music of the Far East – in his case both of Indonesia and Japan. But in several works he's also been influenced by the culture and literature of Spain. His *Very High Kings* (1968), receiving its belated UK premiere in Prom 50, was inspired by the life of Columbus. The title comes from Columbus's letter to the rulers of Spain, Ferdinand and Isabella. The music suggests a spiritual rather than a physical journey (it's subtitled 'from the mystical voyage of Christopher Columbus') and Meale says the music

'The Reception of Christopher Columbus by Ferdinand and Isabella', by Eugene Deveria (1808–65)

A scene from the premiere production of 'Simón Bolívar'
VIRGINIA OPERA/KATHY KEENEY

Thea Musgrave

proceeds 'like a series of visions ... each moving towards fulfilment before giving way to the next'.

Thea Musgrave's opera *Simón Bolívar* deals with the man who liberated South America from Spanish rule three centuries after Columbus. Musgrave was born and educated in Edinburgh but moved to the United States in 1972. Musgrave has written as many as seven operas before *Simón Bolívar*, of which the best-known here is *Mary, Queen of Scots*, first performed at the Edinburgh Festival in 1977. She wrote *Simón Bolívar* originally to a joint commission from Los Angeles Opera (where Domingo was to have premiered the piece), Scottish Opera and the Virginia Opera Association, where her husband Peter Mark is General Director – he conducts excerpts in Prom 45. It's unusual, because Musgrave has composed two different versions side by side, one with English words, the other with Spanish. *Simón Bolívar* was eventually given its first performance in Norfolk, Virginia, in January, to great enthusiasm.

Richard Meale and Malcolm Williamson are almost the same age – they were born in 1932 and 1931 respectively, both in Sydney. Apart from that, their music hasn't much in common, although both composers were influenced early on by Messiaen. Williamson is an eclectic composer, which these days is neither so unusual nor any cause for shame: to be true to yourself as a composer you need not be stylistically consistent. He is also a man of wide sympathies and interests, whose music sometimes reflects not only his Christian faith but his unusually wide-ranging interest in literature. In 1974 Williamson wrote a song-cycle for the Proms called *Hammarskjöld Portrait*, setting poems by the former Secretary General of the United Nations. *A Year of Birds*, his commission this year, sets twelve poems by his friend Iris Murdoch. They describe the seasons and were originally conceived as a calendar; Williamson has grouped them in three movements linked by orchestral episodes. However serious Williamson may be in what he is trying to say, his music has a light touch, and *A Year of Birds* appears in a programme (Prom 36) which begins and ends with Leonard Bernstein.

Hans Werner Henze describes his opulent Eighth Symphony, written for the Boston Symphony Orchestra in 1993, as 'a summer piece'. It might also be described as a set of three orchestral pictures rather than a symphony in the traditional sense. Preceded in

Malcolm Williamson's hand on the score of 'A Year of Birds'

Prom 18 by Mendelssohn's Overture to *A Midsummer Night's Dream*, Henze's symphony is based on three moments in Shakespeare's play: Oberon's instruction to Puck, the comic love scenes between Titania and Bottom, and the final reconciliations of the couples. The mood of poetic enchantment, laced with humour, is typical of the composer, who despite the violence and concern with human struggles in some of his music has always upheld the values of romantic warmth and sensuous appeal.

There's more Henze, his Fourth Symphony of 1955, the previous evening (Prom 17), when Oliver Knussen conducts a programme also including music by Mahler and his own new commission. Knussen calls his conducting career the public part of his life, and says he likes the composing part of it to be private. Yet the two are to some extent linked. He made his conducting debut by taking over the direction of the London Symphony Orchestra from the indisposed István Kertész in his own First Symphony when he was fifteen. It's surely true, also, that Knussen's virtuosity as a composer for the orchestra owes a lot to his conducting experience. Like many composers, he likes to chip away at things, as if the music were lurking mysteriously somewhere and must be approached, discovered, with caution. On and off since 1971 he has been contemplating

Hans Werner Henze

'Titania and Bottom' by Henry Fuseli (1741–1825)

MISHA DONAT

Elliott Carter

and working gradually on a work he likens to Charles Ives's *Universe Symphony*, which never got finished. Part of Knussen's work, an unaccompanied choral piece of eight minutes called *Frammenti da 'Chiara'*, was performed at the Proms in 1986. The title expresses his vision of luminous clarity, a sort of 'heavenly music', and the plan is for orchestral sections in the form of canons, punctuated by what he calls 'book-ends' for a solo soprano with harps. 'The whole thing could be described as a cantata with recitatives and cho-

ruses. But I don't want to give the idea that it's set in stone. If it looks like getting too complicated, I may write a different piece altogether'.

Knussen has conducted a good deal of Elliott Carter's music; he says that Carter's Concerto for Orchestra (1970) has been 'one of the fundamental, ear-opening new musical experiences for many composers of my generation'. Elliott Carter's music certainly established a new standard of some sort: he himself says that his music generally 'seeks the awareness of motion we have in flying or driving a car, and not the plodding of horses or the marching of soldiers that pervade the motion patterns of older music'. His orchestral *Partita*, which the Chicago Symphony brought to London last year, is less thickly scored than much of his earlier music, but it is still very alert, with rapid, strongly outlined gestures and abrupt contrasts. It is the first part of a triptych of which the Prom commission, simply called *Adagio tenebroso* (Prom 66), forms the centre. Sustained, basically slow music is unusual for Carter, though the piece is richly detailed, full of rangy melodic phrases and works up to a dense climax. As the most prestigious American composer of the older generation, and one who still challenges the ears of his listeners more than most, his new piece will be one of the most eagerly awaited premieres of the season.

SPECIAL OFFER VOUCHER

This voucher entitles the bearer to **£3** off
any number and any price of tickets
(not Promenade or Restricted View)
for one of the following twelve Proms:
7·8·17·22·24·27·36·39·49·56·60·64
Subject to availability

SPECIAL OFFER VOUCHER

This voucher entitles the bearer to **£3** off
any number and any price of tickets
(not Promenade or Restricted View)
for one of the following twelve Proms:
7·8·17·22·24·27·36·39·49·56·60·64
Subject to availability

SPECIAL OFFER VOUCHER

This voucher entitles the bearer to **£3** off
any number and any price of tickets
(not Promenade or Restricted View)
for one of the following twelve Proms:
7·8·17·22·24·27·36·39·49·56·60·64
Subject to availability

SPECIAL OFFER VOUCHER

This voucher entitles the bearer to **£3** off
any number and any price of tickets
(not Promenade or Restricted View)
for one of the following twelve Proms:
7·8·17·22·24·27·36·39·49·56·60·64
Subject to availability

SPECIAL OFFER VOUCHER

This voucher entitles the bearer to **£3** off
any number and any price of tickets
(not Promenade or Restricted View)
for one of the following twelve Proms:
7·8·17·22·24·27·36·39·49·56·60·64
Subject to availability

SPECIAL OFFER VOUCHER

This voucher entitles the bearer to **£3** off
any number and any price of tickets
(not Promenade or Restricted View)
for one of the following twelve Proms:
7·8·17·22·24·27·36·39·49·56·60·64
Subject to availability

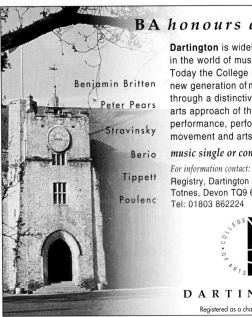

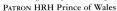

The Malcolm Sargent Cancer Fund for Children

Patron: H.R.H. THE PRINCESS OF WALES

THE MALCOLM SARGENT CENTENARY CONCERT

SPONSORED BY PURA FOOD PRODUCTS LIMITED

GILBERT and SULLIVAN GALA

THE YEOMEN OF THE GUARD

Overture
When our gallant Norman foes
I have a song to sing Oh!
Is life a boon?
Were I thy bride
'Tis done! I am thy bride
Free from his fetters grim
When maiden loves
Strange adventure!

THE PIRATES OF PENZANCE

Poor Wand'ring One
Policeman's Song
Oh! is there not one maiden breast?
When the foeman bares his steel

THE MIKADO

Comes a train of little ladies
Three little maids
A Wand'ring minstrel
Braid the raven hair
The Sun, whose rays are all ablaze
On a tree by a river

THE GONDOLIERS

Overture
Act 1, scene 1
When a merry maiden marries
Take a pair of sparkling eyes
Dance a Cachucha

KATE FLOWERS
soprano

ANNE COLLINS
contralto

DAVID FIELDSEND
tenor

RICHARD LLOYD-MORGAN
baritone

JOHN AYLDON
bass

MALCOLM SARGENT FESTIVAL CHOIR
ROYAL PHILHARMONIC CONCERT ORCHESTRA
Conductor: **CHARLES FARNCOMBE**

ROYAL ALBERT HALL
Sunday 17 September 1995 at 7.30pm

Tickets: Credit card & Telephone Bookings 0171-589 8212 and Agents from 11 May
(postal applications) and 5 June (personal applications) and after 14 August, 14 Abingdon Road,
London W8 6AF. Tel: 0171-937 4547

Grand Tier: £20.00	*Loggia: £13.50*	*Stalls: £15.00*
Second Tier: £10.00	*Front Arena: £10.00*	*Back Arena: £8.50*
Balcony: £6.00		*Balcony (restricted view): £2.00*
	All available in advance	

WORDS BEFORE MUSIC

Stephen Maddock introduces this season's wide range of talks about music

HAD IGOR STRAVINSKY still been alive in 1974, it might have proved difficult for the BBC to persuade him to give a talk before any of the six concerts which featured his music that season. His advice to young composers (as stated in the *New York Review of Books* in 1967) was uncompromising. They should 'not attend culture congresses, not give interviews, not prattle on the radio about music appreciation, not review new scores; and not, either insidiously or directly, push, promote, manoeuvre, advertise, finagle, operate'.

Luckily for the rest of us, very few young composers, or even senior composers, have followed his advice in the last twenty years – at least as far as performances of their music at the Proms have been concerned. The list of those who have spoken to the audience since these talks began two decades ago reads like a roll-call of the great: Berio, Birtwistle, Boulez, Carter, Maxwell Davies, Henze, Lutoslawski, Penderecki, Reich, Tippett and many others.

A Pre-Prom Talk should be more than just a talking programme note; after all, many composers dislike describing their own music in detail. The growth of interest in living composers to which John Drummond refers in his Foreword, and the continuing demands of the classical music 'industry', means that we expect an awful lot of our musicians these days. Not only do they have to be able to play, write or conduct music, they have to be able to talk about it intelligently as well. It is easy to find oneself in the position of having *read* an enormous amount about a composer, but never having *heard* a note of his or her music. So the intention is not that these talks should be an end in themselves, but rather that they (along with the printed programme and the coverage on Radio 3) should provide an aid to listening to and understanding that evening's music.

Given the informal nature of such an occasion a good interviewer can coax a composer into revealing some of the background behind a piece, or put his or her inspirations into context. In 1986, for example, in conversation with John Drummond, Hans Werner Henze revealed an undisclosed programme behind his Seventh Symphony, while last season, before the world premiere of his much-praised Symphony No. 5, Sir Peter Maxwell Davies told a packed Royal College of Music Concert Hall his reasons for describing only some of his large-scale pieces as 'symphonies'. Over the years Sir Peter has given talks about each of his symphonies in turn, and this season he returns to introduce *The Beltane Fire*, his commission for the BBC Philharmonic.

But it is not just brand new pieces that benefit from a little introduction. Sometimes it is equally illuminating to hear a composer's thoughts on how a piece has fared over the years, or to hear one musician's view of another's music. During Pierre Boulez's stint as Chief Conductor of the BBC Symphony Orchestra in the 1970s, for instance, he would discourse on that evening's music before almost every Prom he conducted. In this, his seventieth-birthday year, he returns to introduce his three-part Prom with the BBC Symphony Orchestra, which includes an early work of his own along with masterpieces by Bartók, Debussy and Messiaen.

This year there are more talks than ever before, principally because of the large number of new pieces programmed in this Centenary Season. Most of the composers who have received BBC commissions will be introducing their works, as will also Thomas Adès, Poul Ruders, Bernard Rands, Thea Musgrave, and the fascinating Chinese composer Tan Dun, all of whose pieces are receiving local (rather than world) premieres, while Jonathan Harvey and Nicholas Maw will be discussing music they wrote some time ago.

On the calendar anniversary of the very first Promenade Concert (10 August), the talk will be

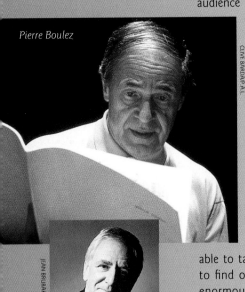

Pierre Boulez

Bernard Rands

CLIVE BARDA/P.A.L.

JEAN BRUBAKER

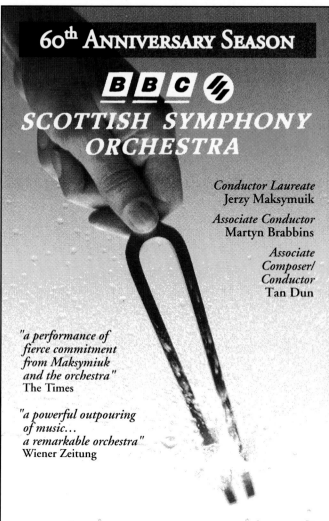

James Crabb

Riccardo Chailly

Esa-Pekka Salonen

Mariss Jansons

given by the outgoing Director, John Drummond, who has been responsible for the last ten seasons. There is also one special innovation: interviews with a handful of the leading international conductors to grace the stage of the Royal Albert Hall this season, including Riccardo Chailly and Mariss Jansons.

The practical arrangements for these talks are simple. You don't need a ticket or a programme to get in, or to have reserved a place in advance. Instead, admission is on a first-come, first-served basis, like the Prom queue itself. Although the queue for the talk doesn't begin as early as the queues for the Arena and Gallery, it is nevertheless *not* a good idea to leave it to the last minute. The Royal College of Music Concert Hall seats only 500 (and Imperial College even fewer), so if you're not there early enough you might not get in. As a rough guide, allowing thirty or forty minutes to queue for a talk is usually enough. There is no admittance to the talk once it has begun. Each talk lasts just half an hour, so there is not generally time to take questions from the audience.

In order to allow people who wish to promenade to come to the talks, they are timed to finish three-quarters of an hour before the concert begins. This gives Promenaders the opportunity to find a good position in the Arena or Gallery, especially as neither of the venues for the talks is more than a couple of minutes' walk from the Albert Hall. So whatever your interest in this season's diet of new and unfamiliar music, why not whet your appetite by coming along to one of these talks?

Pre-Prom Talks for 1995

Tuesday 25 July **Pierre Boulez** 5.45pm
Imperial College Students' Union Concert Hall

Wednesday 26 July **John Casken** 6.15pm
Imperial CU

Thursday 27 July **Sir Peter Maxwell Davies** 5.45pm
Imperial CU

Tuesday 1 August **Thomas Adès** and **Judith Bingham** 5.45pm
Concert Hall, Royal College of Music

Wednesday 2 August **Sally Beamish** 6.15pm RCM

Thursday 3 August **Oliver Knussen** 6.15pm RCM

Friday 4 August **Hans Werner Henze** 5.45pm RCM

Monday 7 August **Lyell Cresswell** and **James Crabb** 5.45pm RCM

Tuesday 8 August **Tan Dun**
Presentation and Education event 5.15pm RCM

Thursday 10 August **Proms Centenary: John Drummond** 6.15pm RCM

Friday 11 August **Judith Weir**
Presentation and Education event 6.00pm RCM

Saturday 12 August **Mariss Jansons** 6.15pm RCM

Monday 14 August **Michael Torke** 6.15pm RCM

Saturday 19 August **Malcolm Williamson** 5.45pm RCM

Monday 21 August **Poul Ruders** 6.15pm RCM

Thursday 24 August **Bernard Rands** 6.15pm RCM

Saturday 26 August **Thea Musgrave** 6.15pm RCM

Tuesday 29 August **Kaija Saariaho** and **Esa-Pekka Salonen** 6.15pm RCM

Thursday 31 August **Edo de Waart** 5.45pm RCM

Monday 4 September **Jonathan Harvey** 6.15pm RCM

Wednesday 6 September **Riccardo Chailly** and **Jan Zekveld** 5.45pm Imperial CU

Thursday 7 September **Steve Reich** 5.45pm Imperial CU

Friday 8 September **Nicholas Maw** 6.15pm Imperial CU

Monday 11 September **James Wood** 6.15pm RCM

Wednesday 13 September **Elliott Carter** 5.45pm RCM

Friday 15 September **Luciano Berio** 6.15pm RCM

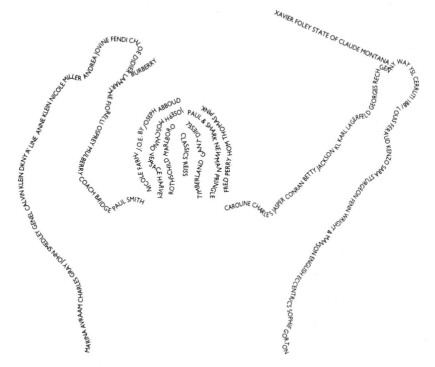

We've got a few maestros of our own.

At Selfridges you'll find scores of top names that are sure to strike a chord – everything from the classic to the avant garde. Forgive us for blowing our own trumpet, but you might say it's the ideal place to conduct your shopping.

SELFRIDGES

OPENING WINDOWS

Phyllida Shaw describes a new joint education project for the Proms involving four of the BBC orchestras

IN THE AUDIENCE for Prom 11 there will be at least eighty composers under the age of seventeen whose music has received a public performance. A concert of their new work, performed by them and by players from four BBC orchestras conducted by Bill Connor, will have taken place an hour or so earlier in the Concert Hall of the Royal College of Music, a couple of minutes from the Royal Albert Hall.

The achievement of these young composers is the result of a collaboration between the BBC's education officers and thirteen players, as well as students from Manchester, London, Cardiff and Glasgow, and the composer Bruce Cole.

Last autumn Cole accepted an invitation from the BBC's orchestras to write a piece for their first joint education project. The commission was to write a skeleton piece with 'windows' which the young composers would fill. The composers would be GCSE music students, who would work with players from their local BBC orchestra, Cole and their music teachers, to fill in the windows and complete the piece.

In 1976 Cole was appointed as the Inner London Education Authority's first composer-in-residence. Since then he has viewed his collaborations with young composers as an essential part of his work. 'I would have been more likely to accept this commission than one purely for the concert hall', he admits. 'One of the problems of being a composer is that so often you take yourself into a room, write the piece, hand it over to the players and the conductor, and that's the last you see of it. In education, on the other hand, I work closely with the players, the students and their teachers.'

'There is still a tremendous focus on the composer as the "lone genius"', Cole claims. 'The search

MUSIC TO OUR EARS

A stylish and sensitive account ... the BBC NOW had something distinctive to say NEW YORK TIMES

Disciplined, polished playing FINANCIAL TIMES

If there has been a better performance of anything all season, I've not heard it THE INDEPENDENT

This magnificent performance by the BBC National Orchestra of Wales ... one was gripped THE TIMES

Cumulatively thrilling THE GUARDIAN

BBC
National
Orchestra of
Wales

*Cerddorfa
Genedlaethol
Gymreig y*
BBC

MUSIC TO YOURS

is always on for the rising star of the next decade. Well, it doesn't have to be like that. The piece you will hear on 29 July will have many composers, and I think a lot of people will be surprised at the standard.'

Cole is thinking of the performance at the Royal College of Music as 'a programme note' to the Prom later that evening. He studied with Sir Harrison Birtwistle, whose *Endless Parade* features in the Prom. Much of Birtwistle's music is based on the idea of varied repetition. Cole has taken variation as his theme for the schools' composition.

The job of organising the project has fallen to the education officers of the participating orchestras and has been co-ordinated by Ann Richards of the Proms Office. Three years ago, none of the orchestras had education specialists; today three of them have full-time staff. Martin Maris of the BBC Philharmonic sees this year's

In May, the players and teachers from the participating schools met for an introductory session with Cole, who explained the task ahead of them. Each window in the piece will be allocated to one school and its group of players. Between May and July, Cole will visit the schools regularly to work with the students, players and teachers to develop the piece. On 29 July the four groups will meet for

BBC Symphony Orchestra Education Project with children from Islington schools

the first time to rehearse the completed work before performing it that evening.

Liz Offerman, the BBC Scottish Symphony Orchestra's freelance Education Officer, is delighted to be participating: 'I see this as a good opportunity for aspiring performers to see beyond the concert platform, to make a contribution to a commission as it's being written, then perform the finished piece. Coupled with that, they will be collaborating with their peers around the rest of the country'.

For Richard Heason of the BBC Symphony the project fits neatly into his programme. 'We have organised many projects like this over the last two years, taking players into different situations and working with a range of groups and communities.

BBC Philharmonic Special Needs Workshop, Cambridgeshire Residency, 1993

Proms project as a significant development. 'Education and community work are increasingly important features of the lives of the BBC orchestras', he says. 'I think the audience at the Royal College of Music will be delighted with the result.'

ALEX VON KOETLITZ

The BBC Symphony Orchestra promotes a large amount of new music and I think it entirely appropriate that we should work with composers in schools. We don't see enough young people in concert audiences. This is an excellent way for them to become involved.'

While not every orchestral player relishes the idea of working with schools, it is an increasingly popular part of many players' lives. For this project the education officers were looking for the right balance of instruments and for players with some experience. Helena Braithwaite of the BBC National Orchestra of Wales has been in post for just two years. In that time, the orchestra has been involved in numerous projects throughout Wales, and she has been struck by their growing enthusiasm.

She believes it is important to demonstrate what an orchestra can contribute to its local community. 'I am very aware that musicians who work full-time in the community have a rather poor impression of orchestras' education work. Many of them think we are doing it simply to enlarge our audiences. I hope this project shows that we really do have a commitment to this work for its own sake.'

Bass player David Langstroth of the BBC National Orchestra of Wales at Cardinal Newman RC Comprehensive School, Pontypridd

Admission to the concert on 29 July is free, though seating is limited.

Further information about the education work of the BBC orchestras can be obtained from:

Richard Heason (BBC SO) 0171-765 2850
Martin Maris (BBC Philharmonic) 0161-200 2171
Helena Braithwaite (BBC NOW) 01222 572069
Liz Offerman (BBC Scottish SO) 0141-338 2606

PETER ROSS

Bassoonist Paul Boyes of the BBC Scottish Symphony Orchestra at Hillhead Primary School, Glasgow, January 1995

The Young Persons' Prom this year is at 11.30am on Sunday 27 August, and will be followed by a picnic in Hyde Park. Tickets for children under 14 will be half-price (except Promenade and Restricted View). For full details, see Prom 46

EDUCATION EVENTS IN THE PROMS

Thursday 27 July
Imperial College Union
11.00am to 12.00 noon
Phil's Live Five
(BBC Philharmonic Workshop)
Phil's Live Five was created by BBC
Philharmonic double bass player Peter
Willmott. He has arranged extracts from
the widest repertoire of well-known music
(and the not-so-well-known), including
Classical, Romantic, Baroque and twentieth-
century, together with jazz, bop, rock, TV
themes, reggae, blues and salsa. If you have
children aged from seven to ten who would
like to participate in a hands-on interactive
percussion workshop, come along to
Imperial College, bringing with you a small
classroom or home-made percussion
instrument (such as a plastic jar with rice
inside). Spaces are limited, so phone
0161-200 2171 to confirm your place.

Saturday 29 July
Royal College of Music
5.45pm to 6.15pm
BBC Orchestras Proms Project
A new composition by Bruce Cole and
students from Whitchurch High School,
North Westminster Community School,
Longdendale High School, and the Junior
Department of the Royal Scottish Academy
of Music. The work will be performed by
members of the BBC Symphony Orchestra,
the BBC Philharmonic, the BBC National
Orchestra of Wales and the BBC Scottish
Symphony Orchestra, conducted by Bill
Connor.

Monday 31 July
Royal College of Music
6.00pm to 6.45pm
Performance by members of the BBC
National Orchestra of Wales of compositions by GCSE and A-level students from
Welsh schools. This project was led by the
composer John Metcalf and members of the
orchestra.

Tuesday 8 August
Royal College of Music
5.15pm to 6.15pm
Composition Project with Tan Dun
Led by Sean Gregory, Paul Griffiths,
Jan Hendricks and Jackie Walduck, with
participants from youth centres in
Waltham Forest.

Friday 11 August
Royal College of Music
6.00pm to 6.45pm
Composition project with Judith Weir
Based on her new Proms commission, with
primary school children and members of the
BBC Symphony Orchestra.

Wednesday 16 August
Royal College of Music
5.30pm to 6.15pm
Presentation and performance involving
students from the RCM and members of
the BBC Symphony Orchestra.

Wednesday 30 August
Royal College of Music
6.00pm to 6.45pm
Performance by members of the BBC
Symphony Orchestra of some of the work
composed as a result of the orchestra's
Young Composers Forum
(sponsored by Land Rover).

Saturday 9 September
Imperial College Union
6.00pm to 6.45pm
Presentation and performance involving
members of the BBC Symphony Orchestra
and RCM students.

ALEX VON KOETTLITZ

THE SOUND OF MANY VOICES

ONE HUNDRED YEARS AGO, the musical backbone of the country was amateur singing. The newly-founded Proms were essentially an orchestral season, but choirs were involved in the early years. The shortage of rehearsal time kept their contribution down, but in the second season they managed 400 voices for Mendelssohn's *Hymn of Praise*, even if Beethoven's 'Choral' Symphony was regularly given without its last, choral, movement until the season of 1929.

This year there are a wide variety of choral Proms with nearly twenty choirs distributed among them. The choirs themselves come at us from two directions. One group has grown up in the intimacy of the wooden oblong of the choir stalls, while the other was born out in the open, in the concert hall.

Most cathedral choirs look back to origins they cannot quite see through the mists of time. The fact that, together with those of the Cambridge and Oxford colleges (such as the Choir of New College,

Oxford), they still exist in a world so profoundly temporal, shows a continuing need.

The function of the choir in worship is the pursuit of excellence: performance at a level which is beyond the reach of the casual member of the congregation. The size of the average choir, and the way it's boxed in by the shape of the place where it sings, underlines that function – to be a part of the ritual as much as the lighting of the candles, or the beauty of the architecture.

It sounds high-minded, but in practice it wasn't always so. A seventeenth-century writer, John Field, thought that cathedrals were 'dens of all loitering lubbers, where squeaking choristers and organ players live in great idleness'. Today the choir of St Paul's Cathedral, which takes part in this year's opening night, as well as the *War Requiem*, has a discipline which it apparently lacked in the mid-nineteenth century, when one visitor noticed that there were only three men in the choir – two altos and a tenor – and that the organ played so loudly that you couldn't hear them.

All that has, of course, changed beyond recognition. Now choirs are free to assume their own identities as their choirmasters direct. Westminster Cathedral Choir, in the hands of George Malcolm, produced a tone in the 1950s that was markedly different from the English Cathedral sound considered ideal for Westminster

Gordon Stewart looks at the traditions of amateur, cathedral and collegiate choirs as reflected in this year's Proms

Village Choir, by Thomas Webster (1800–86)

Top left: *Three clerics singing and a musician playing a viol, early fourteenth century*

Opposite page, top:
Massed choirs singing Handel at the Crystal Palace, 1859

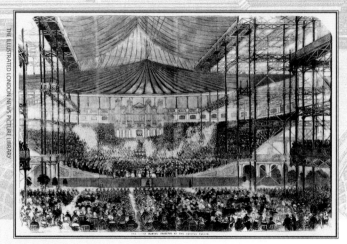

Abbey, just down the road. The choir of Salisbury Cathedral has taken on board the new realities, and has girls as well as boys: with a history now well into its tenth century, its future seems all the more certain for an equal-gender approach.

It was the cathedral and larger parish church choirs which gave most public concerts until the nineteenth century. In *Under the Greenwood Tree* Thomas Hardy's choir is resentful when some of the congregation sing as loudly as they do. But the non-conformists encouraged everyone to sing. There was a general feeling that music did you good – an idea formulated as 'a means of softening the manners, refining the tastes and raising the character of the great body of the people' (the *Westminster Review* in 1841). Singing was cheap, and brought with it the comradeship of fellow choristers and the good-natured competition of other choirs. No town of any size was without its choral society, and no new town hall was built without choir seats in permanent position.

Choirs were started for a variety of reasons. The Bach Choir emerged from the desire of a group of amateurs to study Bach's B minor Mass, but two performances later they decided to perform 'choral works of excellence of various schools'. The London Choral Society was created for the first performance in the capital of Elgar's *Dream of Gerontius*, at Westminster Cathedral in 1903. Both of these venerable groups sing in this year's *War Requiem*.

The choral societies followed their own devices and desires, hiring in orchestras and conductors for their concerts. Now, with choral music planned as part of an overall concert diet, the major symphony orchestras have created their own choirs rather than manoeuvre around the availabilities of choral societies. The predecessor of the Bournemouth Symphony

A Thanksgiving Service at St Paul's Cathedral, 1706

Houses of Parliament present

ALEX VON KOETTLITZ

ALEX VON KOETTLITZ

Top:
The BBC Symphony Chorus

Above: *Stephen Jackson*

Right: *Boy and Girl Choristers of Salisbury Cathedral*

Chorus was one of the first to be put in joint harness with an orchestra. Both were municipal enterprises, designed to supplement each other. Now they have a more open relationship. It's a pattern that recurs. The London Symphony Chorus, for example, remains attached to the London Symphony Orchestra, but the string is loose; similarly with the London Philharmonic Choir.

Even so, a choir whose life is planned around the demands of an orchestral season is different from one following its own primrose path of choral glory. The demands of the orchestra-led repertoire call for singers with specialised skills, including quick reading or learning facility and an ear for languages.

The CBSO Chorus has a heavy schedule, put together on one rehearsal a week, with some extra dates before the concerts. It has tours to fulfil (choirs, like all the best exports, travel well). The Philharmonia Chorus was originally founded as a recording choir, with concerts to prepare for the major dates in the EMI calendar.

The BBC's own choirs obviously have a broadcasting thrust. The BBC Symphony Chorus is carrying the largest part of this season's choral work, as the BBC Symphony Orchestra

does orchestrally. The Chorus is an amateur group, not connected to the BBC Singers, the BBC's two-dozen-strong professional choir. Director Stephen Jackson, who trains and conducts them, notes that 'the Proms are only a fraction of our year's work, but obviously they're the highlight. Choral blockbusters are a thrill for any choir, and this year we have our fair share – Mahler 8 on the First Night, Szymanowski's *Stabat Mater* and the rest – but it's our very own Prom that makes this season special. For a large choir like ours to top the bill is a unique honour, but to be tackling a programme truly at the cutting edge – Ives, Gabrieli and Judith Bingham's new commission – makes it doubly exciting'.

The latest moves are towards youth choirs. The New London Children's Choir, based in North London, has a large membership. Here a double gap is filled: it trains young choristers, on a regular weekly basis, to give concerts of music, some of which is specially commissioned.

Conductors and trainers face the future with enthusiasm and resolve, but things are not by any means sure. There is no doubt that the swing away from school choirs and parish choirs is depriving new generations of vocal stimulation. But the cutbacks in instrumental tuition may yet have the thinnest of silver linings: the free voice we are born with gives us music wherever we go.

PETR BROWN

OPPORTUNITIES FOR CHORISTERS

Choristers from the three London Choir Schools form the children's chorus in Mahler's Symphony No. 8 at the First Night of the Proms. We hope you enjoy their singing!

Do you have a son or pupil who sings well and would enjoy the challenge of becoming a chorister? The Choir Schools offer musically gifted boys the opportunity to participate in the musical heritage of this country and to receive a first-class education. Organists are always ready to meet and advise prospective parents and their sons.

 ST PAUL'S CATHEDRAL CHOIR SCHOOL

C. of E. Foundation
Headmaster: George Hill
Organist and Director of Music: John Scott
40 chorister boarders
60 non-chorister day boys
7-13 years old

The school offers a broad curriculum leading to scholarship and Common Entrance examinations as well as a wide spectrum of games and musical instrument tuition. Chorister boarding fees are heavily subsidised by the Cathedral, and additional bursaries are available for families in need. The choristers are housed on the Cathedral site and are fully integrated with the day-boys for academic studies. Voice trials are held in February, May and October for boys of 6¾ and upward.

Further details from the Headmaster, St. Paul's Cathedral Choir School, New Change, London
EC4M 9AD
Tel: 0171 248 5156

 WESTMINSTER ABBEY CHOIR SCHOOL

C. of E. Foundation
Headmaster: Gordon Roland-Adams
Organist and Master of the Choristers: Martin Neary
38 chorister boarders
8-13 years old.

The only school in the country reserved exclusively for the education of boy choristers. A comprehensive refurbishment has recently been undertaken, providing excellent facilities, whilst retaining the character of the much-loved Edwardian building. In addition to the usual academic subjects and sporting activities, all boys learn two musical instruments, and the recent record of scholarships to senior schools has been impressive. Voice trials for the valuable scholarships are held in February, May and October.

Further details from the Headmaster, Westminster Abbey Choir School, Dean's Yard, London
SW1P 3NY
Tel: 0171 222 6151

 WESTMINSTER CATHEDRAL CHOIR SCHOOL

Roman Catholic Foundation
Headmaster-elect: Charles Foulds
Master of Music: James O'Donnell
30 chorister boarders
60 non-chorister day boys
8-13 years old

Voice trials are held every term for Roman Catholic boys aged between 7 and 9 years. Valuable scholarships are offered to choristers, who then normally go on to win music and/or academic awards to their next school. Additional bursaries are available in case of need. The school is situated in the Cathedral precincts and has a first-rate academic and musical tradition, along with excellent sports and recreation facilities.

Further details from the Headmaster, Westminster Cathedral Choir School, Ambrosden Avenue, London
SW1P 1QW
Tel: 0171 798 9081

TRINITY
college of music:

Trinity

- is one of the country's foremost music conservatoires
- is located in the heart of London's West End
- prepares students for a professional career in music
- has a long tradition of performance at the centre of all its study provision
- provides regular concert and opera performance opportunities for students at a variety of London venues

Undergraduate and Postgraduate performing courses

- Individual tuition and performance activities
- Four year full time **BMus (TCM)** course
- Three year full time **BMus (London)** course
- One year **Postgraduate Certificate in Performance/ Composition**
- One year **MMus (London)**
  For a Prospectus, please contact *the College Registrar*.

Music Education Services

The Music Education Department has a range of short and vacation courses held throughout the UK, for music teachers wishing to refresh their knowledge. Most courses carry accreditation leading to professional music education qualifications at Certificate and Diploma levels. Further details from *the Administrator, Music Education Department*.

Junior Department

Trinity College's Junior Department offers talented youngsters individual lessons and a range of group activities, choirs and orchestras through its thriving Saturday school. For details, please contact *the Registrar, Junior Department*.

 TRINITY COLLEGE OF MUSIC
Mandeville Place London W1M 6AQ
Tel. 0171 935 5773 Fax. 0171 224 6278
Principal : Gavin Henderson

VERDI
FESTIVAL

12 June - 22 July

Verdi Festival includes:

Un ballo in maschera
Stiffelio
I due Foscari new production
Simon Boccanegra
La traviata

Roberto Alagna in recital
Aroldo in concert
Simon Boccanegra
in concert at the Queen Elizabeth Hall

and many additional associated events.

Painting of Giuseppe Verdi by Stephen Martin

For a free leaflet phone the Mailing List Department on 0171-240 1200 extension 123.

The ROYAL OPERA

ROYAL OPERA HOUSE ◆ 0171-304 4000

NFMS AT 60

JOIN THE NATIONAL FEDERATION OF MUSIC SOCIETIES AS IT CELEBRATES SIXTY YEARS OF LIVE MUSIC PROMOTION

NFMS represents 1,500 choirs, orchestras and concert promoters nationwide. It provides financial, artistic and training services and ensures that the value of the voluntary music sector is recognised.

23 February *(the sixtieth anniversary to the day of the founding of the NFMS in York)* **Celebratory Evensong in York Minster and Concert**

4 May Symphony Hall, Birmingham **Diamond Jubilee Celebratory Gala Concert with José Carreras**

15 July Berlioz Grande Messe des Morts, a one-day workshop and concert at Imperial College, London.

29 September – 1 October Diamond Jubilee National Conference University of York

1935·1995
JUBILEE
NATIONAL · FEDERATION OF · MUSIC · SOCIETIES

• 12 regional Jubilee Celebration Concerts • National lottery with dozens of prizes • Sponsored Bike Ride from London to York • Hundreds of members' celebration concerts

For further details of all the Federation's Diamond Jubilee events please call the Diamond Jubilee Information line on 0171-233 9969

HMV

EXPERT ASSISTANCE
from
EXPERT ASSISTANTS

You won't just find classical trained staff at HMV but classically trained musicians.

After all who better to ask about classical music than a classical musician?

Plus there is over 75 years experience of classical music to play on too.

Our huge and extensive stock covers all aspects of fine music including the entire British catalogue.

And if what you're looking for isn't on display we'll order it for you even if it means importing it from all over the world.

We also have a credit card ordering facility. Simply ring 0171-631 3423 for more details.

HMV 150 OXFORD STREET • THE WORLD'S BIGGEST MUSIC STORE • ALSO AT 363 OXFORD STREET (BOND STREET TUBE)

KNOW HMV • KNOW MUSIC

INDEX OF WORKS

* First performance at a Henry
Wood Promenade Concert

Arvo Pärt

MALCOLM CROWTHERS

Magnar Åm

Play an instrumental part in the Royal Marines.

If you're male or female, sixteen to twenty-eight years of age, love music, and have an aptitude to play one or two instruments, then ATTENTION.

The Royal Marines Band Service is currently looking for candidates to enrol for a select number of places at the Royal Marines School of Music.

You'll receive over two years' training to a very high standard in a variety of instruments. As well as traditional military band music, you will earn as you learn to play jazz, pop, classical, light concert and big band music. You could find yourself taking part in the Edinburgh Festival, Beating Retreat on Horse Guards Parade or even a Cup Final at Wembley. So, if you're looking for your musical career to move up a scale or two, call us today on **0345 300 123** or return the coupon. Hurry, the closing date is soon. So **MOVE IT, MOVE IT, MOVE IT.**

Send to Naval Careers Service, Department (MA96818), FREEPOST 4335, Bristol BSI 3YX. No stamp needed.
Please send me your free information pack on careers in the Royal Marines Band Service. I understand I am under no obligation.

NAME (Mr, Mrs, Miss)

ADDRESS

POSTCODE   DATE OF BIRTH

TELEPHONE

We are equal opportunities employers under the Race Relations Act and welcome enquiries and applications from all ethnic groups. Normally you should have been a UK resident for the past five years.

ROYAL MARINES
BAND SERVICE

See the world. Differently.

Jonathan Harvey

JOHN CAREWE

Judith Weir

MALCOLM CROWTHERS

György Ligeti

LOU STONE

WH Smith and EMI present.........

The EMI Classics Collection

An excellent introduction to the vast treasures of classical music.

A range of 20 titles on CD and cassette.

Only available from WH Smith music stockists.

CD's £7.99   Cassettes £4.99 each.

WH SMITH

Michael Torke

Nicholas Maw

John Tavener

Oxford

For excellence in the publishing of choral works and collections, scholarly editions, educational and tutorial music, and an internationally-performed contemporary list

Highlights include:

Boris Godunov

The C P E Bach Edition

Tudor Church Music

Carols for Choirs Series

New Oxford Book of Carols

Oxford Books of Madrigals

National Curriculum Courses

Oxford Primary Music

Guitar Styles!

Oxford Piano Method

Strings in Step

Fauré Requiem

Mozart Requiem

Haydn Creation

Oxford Choral Classics

Oxford University Press
Music Department
Walton Street
Oxford OX2 6DP

Tel: 01865 56767
Fax: 01865 267749

OUP COMPOSERS

- Eleanor Alberga
- Gerald Barry
- Michael Berkeley
- Benjamin Britten
- John Buller
- Martin Butler
- Andrew Carter
- Gordon Crosse
- Michael Finnissy
- Roberto Gerhard
- Edward Harper
- Alun Hoddinott
- Constant Lambert
- Libby Larsen
- William Mathias
- Elis Pehkonen
- Gerald Plain
- Anthony Powers
- Alan Rawsthorne
- John Rutter
- Robert Sherlaw Johnson
- Howard Skempton
- Hilary Tann
- Phyllis Tate
- Ralph Vaughan Williams
- William Walton

Sir Michael Tippett

JASON SHENAI

Iannis Xenakis

MALCOLM CROWTHERS

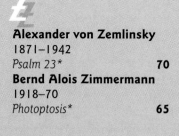

Malcolm Williamson

MALCOLM CROWTHERS

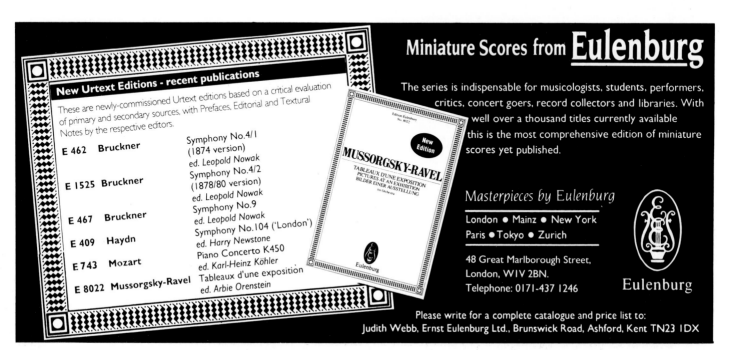

THE PROMS IN PICTURES

To celebrate the Centenary of the Proms, BBC Concerts Publications, who also bring you the Proms Guide and the Proms programmes, are releasing a splendid souvenir book.

The Proms in Pictures traces the 100-year history of the Proms with photographs of the people, places and events that have made the Proms the world's greatest music festival.

An attractive collectors' item, *The Proms in Pictures* will be on sale from June 1995 at all good bookshops, priced £5.99.

PHOTO BY GODFREY MACDOMNIC